IRELAND'S BIRDS

IRELAND'S BIRDS

THEIR DISTRIBUTION AND MIGRATIONS

BY

ROBERT F. RUTTLEDGE

H. F. & G. WITHERBY LTD

61/62 WATLING STREET, LONDON E.C.4

First published in 1966

Made and printed in Great Britain by
William Clowes and Sons, Limited
London and Beccles

CONTENTS

LIST OF ILLUSTRATIONS

IRELAND
10°
9°
8°
7°
6°
55°
54°
INISHTRAHULL
MALIN Hd.
Trawbreaga Bay
TORY I.
HORN Hd.
L. Swilly
INCH
L. Foyle
RATHLIN I.
FAIR Hd.
ARANMORE
Derryveagh Mts.
LONDONDERRY
LONDONDERRY
R. Bann
MAIDENS L.Ho.
ROANINISH
DAWROS Hd.
DONEGAL
LIFFORD
Sperrin Mts.
BALLYMENA
LARNE
Larne L.
ANTRIM
L. Beg
ANTRIM
Slieve Tooey
RATHLIN O'BIRNE L. Ho.
Slieve League
DONEGAL
OMAGH
TYRONE
Lough Neagh
Belfast L.
COPELAND I.
BANGOR
BELFAST
Donegal Bay
U L S T E R
Strangford
L. Erne
INISHMURRAY
L. Melvin
STAGS OF BROADHAVEN
Killala Bay
ENNISKILLEN
ARMAGH
DOWN
DOWNPATRICK
ERRIS Hd.
LISSADELL
FERMANAGH
BELMULLET
Sligo Bay
SLIGO
LEITRIM
MONAGHAN
ARMAGH
ST. JOHN'S Pt.
INISHGLORA
Upr. L. Erne
Dundrum Bay
Blacksod Bay
L. Carrowmore
INISHKEA
THE MULLET
Ox Mts.
SLIGO
Mourne Mts.
BLACK ROCK L. Ho.
BALLINA
L. Allen
MONAGHAN
Nephin Mt.
R. Moy
L. Arrow
R. Shannon
DUVILLAUN I.
L. Conn
L. Key
CAVAN
Carlingford L.
ACHILL I.
CAVAN
DUNDALK
Dundalk Bay
MAYO
CASTLEBAR
L. Gara
L. Boderg
L. Sheelin
LOUTH
Clew Bay
CLARE I.
WESTPORT
CONNACHT
CLAREMORRIS
ROSCOMMON
LONGFORD
LONGFORD
R. Boyne
DROGHEDA
INISHTURK
L. Carra
AN UAIM
BALBRIGGAN
INISHBOFIN
L. Mask
ROSCOMMON
MEATH
INISHARK
Inny R.
L. Owell
Rogerstown Estuary
Twelve Bens
L. Ree
WEST MEATH
LAMBAY I.
CONNEMARA
R. Clare
TUAM
L. Funshinagh
MULLINGAR
SWORDS
MALAHIDE
SLYNE Hd.
L. Corrib
R. Suck
ATHLONE
L. Ennell
DUBLIN
HOWTH Hd.
GALWAY
R. Shannon
R. Brosna
NORTH BULL I.
DUBLIN
Dublin Bay
GALWAY

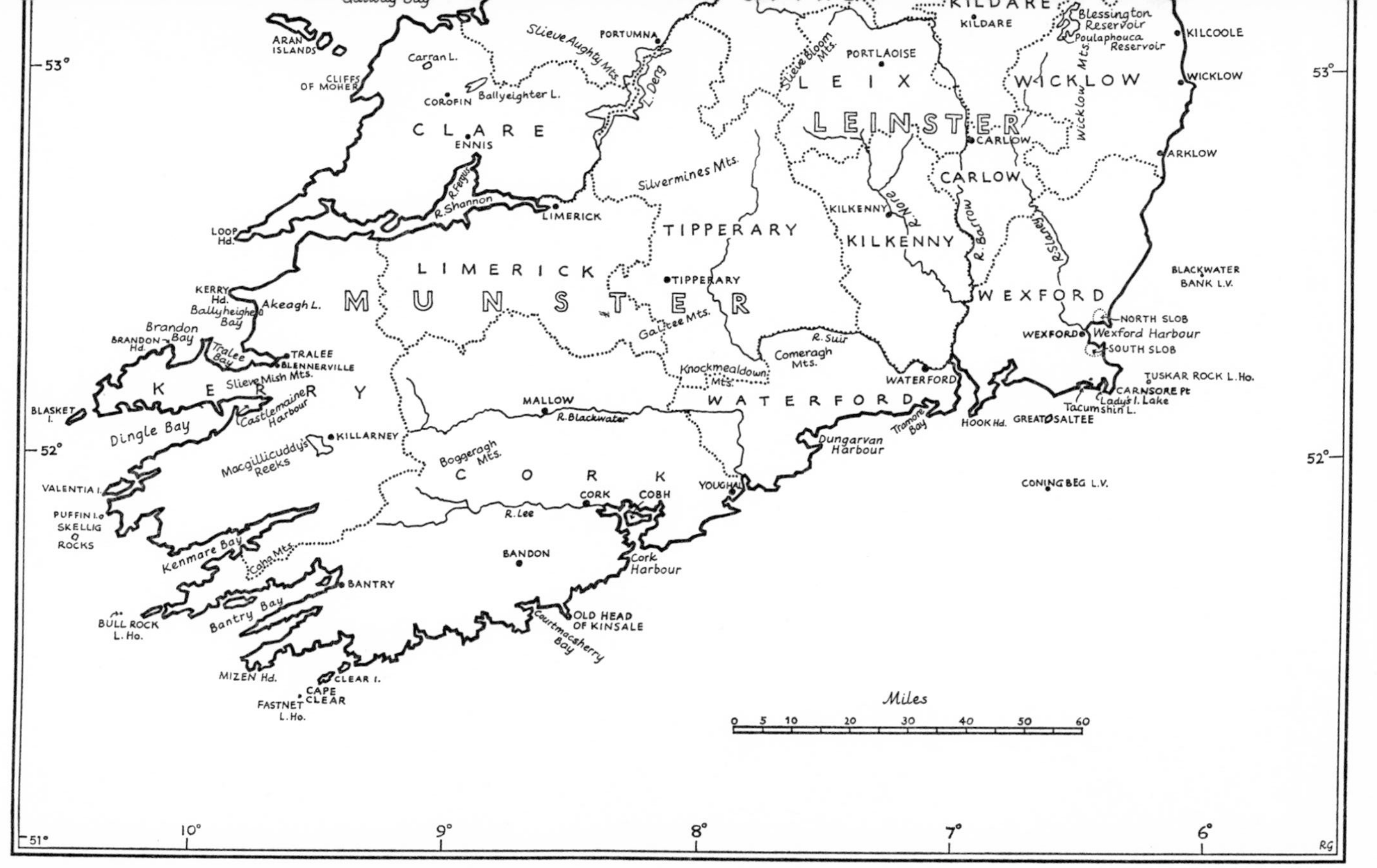

ARAN ISLANDS
CLIFFS OF MOHER
Carran L.
COROFIN
Ballyeighter L.
CLARE
ENNIS
Slieve Aughty Mts.
PORTUMNA
L. Derg
R. Fergus
R. Shannon
LIMERICK
LOOP Hd.
KERRY Hd.
Ballyheigh Bay
Akeagh L.
Brandon Bay
BRANDON Hd.
Tralee Bay
TRALEE
BLENNERVILLE
Slieve Mish Mts.
KERRY
BLASKET I.
Castlemaine Harbour
Dingle Bay
KILLARNEY
Macgillicuddy's Reeks
VALENTIA I.
PUFFIN I.
SKELLIG ROCKS
Kenmare Bay
Caha Mts.
BANTRY
Bantry Bay
BULL ROCK L. Ho.
MIZEN Hd.
CLEAR I.
CAPE CLEAR
FASTNET L. Ho.
LIMERICK
MUNSTER
Silvermines Mts.
TIPPERARY
TIPPERARY
Galtee Mts.
Knockmealdown Mts.
Comeragh Mts.
R. Suir
MALLOW
R. Blackwater
Boggeragh Mts.
CORK
CORK
COBH
R. Lee
BANDON
Cork Harbour
YOUGHAL
OLD HEAD OF KINSALE
Courtmacsherry Bay
WATERFORD
WATERFORD
Dungarvan Harbour
Tramore Bay
HOOK Hd.
GREAT SALTEE
KILDARE
KILDARE
PORTLAOISE
Slieve Bloom Mts.
LEIX
LEINSTER
CARLOW
CARLOW
KILKENNY
KILKENNY
R. Nore
R. Barrow
R. Slaney
WEXFORD
WEXFORD
Wexford Harbour
NORTH SLOB
SOUTH SLOB
TUSKAR ROCK L. Ho.
CARNSORE Pt
Lady's I. Lake
Tacumshin L.
CONINGBEG L.V.
BLACKWATER BANK L.V.
Blessington Reservoir
Poulaphouca Reservoir
KILCOOLE
WICKLOW
WICKLOW
Wicklow Mts.
ARKLOW
Miles
0 5 10 20 30 40 50 60
53°
52°
51°
10°
9°
8°
7°
6°
RG

ACKNOWLEDGMENTS

To all the following I am most grateful—Those who sent their records to the *Irish Bird Reports* and to others who have assessed records when expert advice was sought. Their names are too numerous to mention, but can be found listed in the issues of the *Irish Bird Report*. Without the willing submission of these records this book could not have been written.

George Waterson for his enthusiastic help at the inception of the book, similarly P. A. D. Hollom and for his advice on contents and for commenting on the draft of my two essays.

I. J. Ferguson-Lees for assistance in several directions, and the staff of the Natural History Division of the National Museum for unfailing help and courtesy. C. D. Deane, J. S. Jackson and F. King for kindly writing special articles.

The article on the Wildfowl Situation in Ireland is reprinted by courtesy of the Nature Conservancy and the International Wildfowl Research Bureau from the Proceedings of the First European Meeting on Wildfowl Conservation.

I am much indebted to those who have in some cases at considerable trouble to themselves, provided the photographs—David Cabot for those on Plates 1, 2, 7a, 8b, and two of those on Plate 11; Ian Finlay for those on Plates 3, 6, 8a, and one illustration on Plate 11; The Irish Tourist Board for those on Plates 4, 5 and 9; The Northern Ireland Tourist Board for that on Plate 10; Rex Roberts Studios for the photograph of Great Saltee, Plate 7b.

I am indeed grateful for the excellent map which Robert Gillmor has specially prepared for the book.

I wish to thank my publishers, H. F. and G. Witherby, Ltd., and particularly Antony Witherby for his help throughout, and in many knotty problems.

Mrs. A. Ludvik I thank for having so efficiently wrestled with my handwriting to produce most accurate typescript.

I am more than grateful to my wife for encouragement on occasions when my enthusiasm for the work has flagged, and for help in many ways.

ROBERT F. RUTTLEDGE

INTRODUCTION

To follow one book on the birds of a country after only twelve years by another might seem superfluous.

When *Birds of Ireland* (1954) was written it was very necessary for there had been no books of this nature since 1900. Moreover, there had been changes in the status and distribution of some species, and also an increase in knowledge.

The book of 1954 served to stimulate interest and the need to fill gaps in our knowledge. Indeed, some gaps still remain. Added stimulus has been given by the *Irish Bird Report* which is published annually and helps to keep our knowledge up to date. It will continue to be published for this purpose.

As a result of the interest aroused there is, nowadays, a far more widespread band of observers, though even now they are thin enough upon the ground. Undoubtedly this increased observer strength has accounted for many additional records.

The *Irish Bird Reports* have continued to fulfil their original objective and now, after twelve years, the time has come to make use of the information collected.

It is nowadays impossible, except under special circumstances, to produce a book on the voluminous scale that was thought essential in earlier times. This book therefore has been made as concise as possible, giving the general distribution and outline of the migration of the commoner species. Rather more detail is given concerning vagrant species. In the case of those birds which have been reported ten times or less, all details are given as far as they are known.

In order not to burden the text with constant references, these have been omitted except in about two cases where to trace them might be difficult.

The descriptions in support of the occurrences of rare birds seen since 1954 will be found in the *Irish Bird Reports*, Nos. 1–13. In one or two cases where the validity of a species was under discussion at the time of publication the description occurs under the species in the *Report* of a subsequent year. Otherwise, the description is found in the *Report* for the year in which the bird was reported.

All records given in *Birds of Ireland* (1954) have been carefully re-assessed.

A critical attitude has been adopted. In any case where a record in *Birds of Ireland* (1954) or submitted for publication in the *Irish Bird Reports* did not measure up to the 100% certainty required it was rejected. It has been found preferable to exclude some records which may, in fact, have been perfectly sound, rather than err on the lenient side.

Square brackets have been used as little as possible. Lack of space has prevented any lengthy discussion for their reason or omission. Reference to previous works on Irish birds will help to clarify the assessment, and this is especially so in the cases of a few species now left unbracketed; if need be, posterity can judge for themselves.

Certain species square-bracketed in former works have been omitted entirely where it is clear that the bird was not indigenous (*e.g.* Tawny Owl, Marsh Tit, Nuthatch) nor a true vagrant.

Finally, there are some records which have been controversial. Among these are included those of the Kumlien's Gull, Royal Tern, Passenger Pigeon, Belted Kingfisher and Slate-coloured Junco. In these cases all available evidence has been carefully studied and where the conclusion arrived at has been satisfactory, the record has been included.

Conversely, a few records admitted over the years have now been discarded. A number of reports published in the public press or in non-ornithological literature from unreliable sources have been omitted.

In dealing with each species the greatest possible uniformity has been aimed at.

Thus for each species there is a general *status* heading, then follows more detailed distribution.

'Resident' indicates that the species is found in Ireland the year round and that it breeds.

'Passage Migrant' is used to show that a species passes along our coasts or through the country, bound for a destination beyond Ireland. In some cases there is little or no clear-cut evidence and in these cases the expression 'Passage migrant and/or immigrant' is used.

'Vagrant' denotes that a species is more in the nature of a casual visitor and where a species appears fairly often it is termed an 'Irregular visitor'.

For species that are purely accidental and for which there are ten records or less, the number of records is given and each is detailed.

'Summer visitors' are immigrants that come to breed. A few species are described as non-breeding summer visitors.

'Winter visitor' refers to species that arrive in autumn and winter, then depart in spring.

Migration information includes times of arrival and departure, peak periods of passage or other movements, and unusual dates for some species. In some cases knowledge derived from ringing results is given.

Wherever possible actual numbers are given in preference to the more vague terms.

Species are arranged in the order of the *B.O.U. Check List* (1952) but with the changes recommended in *British Birds*, Vol. 46. The English nomenclature follows that used in *British Birds*.

All records available up to the end of 1965 have been included, and the *status* of all species as at the present. Development, drainage, excessive shooting, pesticides, toxic chemicals and water pollution are, unfortunately, already showing adverse effects on the bird population and some species are becoming less numerous or even scarce.

THE TOPOGRAPHY OF IRELAND, WITH BRIEF DESCRIPTIONS OF BIRD HABITATS

JOHN S. JACKSON, M.A., PH.D.

Topographically, Ireland can be divided conveniently into four well-defined regions, the coastal region, the central lowland, the upland and the mountainous areas.

Coastal Region

The coastline of Ireland is a drowned shore-line and the effects of this submergence can be seen in the drowned valleys, or rias, of many of the major rivers around the coasts, the Barrow estuary, the Bandon River, the Kenmare River, the River Moy, etc. The drowned valleys have, in most cases, been filled by great thicknesses of glacial deposits of clays and gravels which, with recent river deposits, produce broad, shallow estuaries with extensive estuarine swamps, marshes and sloblands with salt-marshes which hold large numbers of geese, duck and waders. The most famous slobs on the Irish coasts are the North and South Slobs bordering Wexford harbour; these are typical examples and are partly artificial in origin, their present existence being due to the construction of dykes and the introduction of pumping stations.

On all coasts there are numerous sand spits which frequently impound a lagoon with an associated salt-marsh which supports a considerable population of duck, waders and terns. Such lagoons occur in the Dublin area, Malahide and the North Bull Island, and in Co. Wicklow, the Kilcoole Marsh and the Murrough, which are impounded by an extensive storm beach. These lagoons are best seen in Co. Wexford where sand spits have impounded extensive brackish lakes at Lady's Island Lake and Lake Tacumshin. On the west coast sand spits commonly develop in the long bays, beautifully seen in Dingle Bay with the dual spits of Rosbeigh and Inch and also at Fenit. In Killala Bay, Bartragh Island is connected to the mainland by a sand spit, which protects the inshore mudflats of the Moy estuary, with their flocks of waders and diving ducks, from the direct effects of heavy seas, which outside the bar are often turbulent and are favoured by Common Scoters and Long-tailed Duck. The great inlets on the east and west of the Inishowen peninsula in Co. Donegal, Lough Foyle and Lough Swilly respectively, are of considerable ornithological importance.

Off-shore bars and banks have been produced in the Irish Sea by the pushing effects of an ice sheet which moved down the Irish Sea basin during Pleistocene times, gouging out enormous masses of marine sediments towards the shore line. These ridges of material now form banks parallel to the coastline; they are extremely shallow at low tide and carry considerable numbers of scoters. Such banks fringe the east coast between the Boyne estuary and Skerries in north Co. Dublin, the Dublin coast, and off the Wicklow and east Wexford coasts.

High sea-cliffs which are comparatively rare on the east coast provide cliffs suitable for such sea birds as Guillemots, Kittiwakes, Puffins, gulls and Fulmars. The south coast has many fine, though low, cliffs, approximately 200 feet high, such as those on the Great Saltee Island and on the Waterford coast west of Tramore. The sea-cliffs of Co. Cork west of Cork Harbour and those of the Kerry coast support a fluctuating population of Choughs. The finest sea-cliff scenery in Ireland is in Co. Clare, the Cliffs of Moher (688′), Inishmore in the Aran Island group, Clare Island (800′), Achill Island, Menawn Cliffs (800′), in Co. Mayo, Slieve League (1,972′) and Slieve Tooey (about 1,000′) in Co. Donegal; all have a variety and abundance of cliff-breeding birds. The Antrim basalts provide impressive cliff scenery at Benbane Head and at Fair Head, where the golden eagle nested in recent years, and also on Rathlin Island. These sea-cliffs are good resorts for auks and Kittiwakes. Sea-stacks occur around the coasts but particularly on the west, where the Skelligs and Tearaght off the Kerry coast, and the Stags of Broad Haven, off north-west Mayo, are well-known examples and which hold colonies of Manx Shearwaters, Storm Petrels, Puffins and auks.

The blanket bogs of the west of Ireland belong essentially to the coastal region. The distribution of this particular bog type is controlled by several factors, including mean annual rainfall, number of rain days per annum and concentration of chlorides in the atmosphere. This type of bog, as the name suggests, blankets extensive areas from sea-level to considerable heights on the uplands and presents great areas of undulating, unrelieved bog-land. The vegetation is fundamentally different to that of the raised bogs of the midlands, *Molinia* (flying bent) being an important element. This type of vegetation, essentially lacking the fraochan or bilberry and other important elements of the raised bog flora, is characterised by an impoverished bird population. White-fronted Geese are associated with the western blanket bogs and feed on the roots of bog-cotton (*Eriophorum angustifolium*). Some Golden Plover breed.

The Lowland Area

This area is topographically diverse and extends from the east coast to the west, meeting the Atlantic at Galway Bay, Sligo Bay and Donegal Bay. Diversity of topographical features include the following:

Raised bogs:

These form a vast area of extensive, anastomosing and coalescing boglands which, between Dublin and Galway, are collectively known as the Bog of Allen complex. This midland area of maximum raised bog development is sensibly delimited by the 40″ rainfall line (isohyet), other factors controlling the development of these bogs being mean annual rainfall and the number of rain days per annum. Farther west, in an area of higher rainfall, the raised, midland-type bog is replaced by the western-type blanket bog. The raised bogs have a rich and characteristic flora in which mosses, e.g., *Sphagnum*, predominate. Plants of food value to birds include bog-cotton (*Eriophorum angustifolium*), heath (*Erica tetralix*), and heather (*Calluna vulgaris*) on the drier parts of the bog, and fraochan or bilberry (*Vaccinium myrtillus*), etc. The birds associated with the raised bogs of the midlands include White-fronted Geese, Curlew, Snipe, Grouse and insectivorous birds such as Meadow Pipits, Skylarks and Stonechats and locally Whinchats.

Lakes:

(a) Lakes of the limestone region: Many of the large lakes of the central lowland occur in Carboniferous Limestone areas and are, in many cases, of chemical solution origin. These lakes are of considerable area, often fringed by extensive reed beds (*Phragmites communis* and the reed-mace, *Typha latifolia*) and rushes (*Scirpus lacustris*). The waters are alkaline with abundant bottom feeding. Examples of such lakes are Lough Owel and Lough Derravaragh in Co. Westmeath, Lough Sheelin to the north, Lough Ree and Lough Derg on the River Shannon and Lough Corrib and Lough Mask in Connaught, the last two being bounded by acid rocks on their western sides and the associated flora differing fundamentally in consequence. Lough Carra, adjoining Lough Mask and completely floored by limestone, is extremely shallow with excellent bottom feeding and supports a large population of diving ducks.

(b) Turloughs: These are temporary, or intermittent, lakes which occupy very shallow solution depressions in the Carboniferous Limestone and are abundant in the north Clare-south Galway and south Mayo area. The bottoms of these lakes lie above the level of the summer water table so that during periods of reduced rainfall or drought, with a correspondingly depressed regional water table, the water level within the lakes falls, the water escaping through solution fissures in the limestone joints and the lake 'disappears'. During winter months, as the rainfall increases, the regional water table rises above the level of the lake floor, the water floods into the depression through the solution fissures and the turlough 'reappears'. An assemblage of very short grasses forms a dense sward on areas of level limestone which are periodically submerged. The vegetation harbours a rich aquatic fauna on which birds feed and the turloughs being usually shallow support large numbers of waders, duck and swans, both Whooper and Bewick's.

(c) Lakes associated with the drumlin belt: The drumlin belt is a zone of small, grass-covered hills of glacial origin extending from Co. Down, through Cavan, Longford and north Co. Meath to Co. Mayo; many of the islands of Clew Bay are partially submerged drumlins. These hills, which are of semi-ovoid shape, are sometimes so numerous in an area as to present a fanciful resemblance to a basketful of eggs. Drumlin formation leads to impeded regional drainage and small lakes are frequently impounded in the 'slacks' between the drumlins. The lake waters are characteristically alkaline and offer ideal conditions for the development of a fen vegetation of *Phragmites* reeds, rushes and sedges, which are frequented especially by Great Crested Grebes, Coots, Moorhens and a variety of duck.

(d) Kettle holes: Kettle holes are shallow depressions, frequently a mere hundred yards or so in diameter, which are scattered through the central lowland on good agricultural land. Small patches of rushes and reeds are usually associated with them. These ponds often hold a sprinkling of surface-feeding duck. The kettle holes originate by large lumps of stagnant ice becoming incorporated into the boulder clays; as the ice melts a depression remains and, being floored by impermeable clays, rain water accumulates in them. Although natural features, they closely resemble artificial dew ponds in shape and size.

Rivers: Many of the large rivers have extensive fringing beds of rushes with reed-mace and 'flaggers' or yellow iris. These hold large numbers of Moorhens, Water Rails and Coots and, in season, Mallard, Teal and Wigeon. Sedge Warblers and Reed Buntings frequent the reed beds. Extensive *Phragmites* reed beds develop in marshy areas coinciding with vegetation-choked cut-offs of the main river and are frequented by duck, Snipe and vagrant Bitterns. Such rivers are the Barrow and Nore, the Cork Blackwater, the Bandon River, etc.

Wooded areas: Throughout the central lowland there are many cultivated woodlands, usually associated with estate lands, which carry a number of Woodcock, Woodpigeons, Rooks, Jays and a variety of passerines, including the warblers in summer.

Karst area: The karst area of bare limestone extends intermittently from Co. Clare, south of Corofin, through Co. Galway and into Co. Roscommon. The typical arboreal vegetation of this area is hazel scrub and copses (*Corylus avellana*), with a tangled undergrowth of bracken, brambles and fraochan, or bilberry. The vegetation provides an ideal habitat for Woodcock and passerines, including warblers in summer.

Uplands

This area comprises rolling terrain above the 1,000-foot contour. It includes the Tertiary plateau basalts of Co. Antrim, the Sperrin Mountains, much of the granites of the Dublin and Wicklow hills, the isolated upfolded hills of the central lowland, the Slieve Blooms, etc., and, in the south, parts of the Galtees, the Comeraghs, etc., all of which consist of flanking Old Red Sandstone with, in places, a breached core of older slates and grits. The Millstone Grit (Upper Carboniferous) also gives rise to upland country, as in the Castlecomer plateau and Slieve Ardagh and the hills surrounding Lough Allen. The vegetation is poor and much of the area is covered by a mantle of high-level blanket bog which, vegetationally, is distinct from the low-level, western-type blanket bog. On the drier ground the vegetation includes sheep's fescue, mat grass, upland gorse (*Ulex galii* as opposed to the gorse of lower altitudes, *Ulex europaea*), bilberry or fraochan and scattered sedges. The vegetation provides excellent cover for Grouse while Snipe are found in the wetter parts. Scattered pairs of Ring Ouzels are to be seen in steep, boulder-strewn valleys and Ravens are not uncommon. The Merlin is associated with this region as is also the occasional Peregrine. Corrie lakes occur in the cirques of the upland area but the waters are typically acid, with little vegetational cover at the margins, and therefore few birds.

The Mountain Region

This is an area of spectacular topographical relief which frequently merges with the upland area and extends from the higher parts of the uplands to altitudes of over 3,000 feet. Mountainous areas in Ireland include parts of the Wicklow hills (Lugnaquilla, 3,039′), Mount Leinster, the Macgillycuddy Reeks (Carrantuohill, 3,414′), the Twelve Bens in Connemara, Nephin in Mayo, Errigal in Donegal and the Mourne Mountains in Co. Down. The underlying geology is characteristically acid, Old Red Sandstone, quartzite and granite, and the vegetation is correspondingly poor. Much of the mountainous area, the precipitous back cliffs of cúms or corries and the scree slopes, are virtually devoid of vegetation. Bird life is extremely rare in these regions but includes such birds as Ravens and the occasional Peregrine.

NORTHERN IRELAND AND ITS BIRDS

C. DOUGLAS DEANE, F.M.A.
Deputy Director, Ulster Museum

Both Ireland and Scotland share the same physical history, especially in the north of Ireland where the three main structural divisions of highland, central lowland and southern upland, have extended south-westwards into Ireland. Two factors more than any other which have affected the distribution of birds in the north-east are the intrusion of igneous rocks and the action of ice which resulted in the series of whale-backed ridges which stretch across Northern Ireland from the Down coast to Fermanagh.

Northern Ireland is a political region rather than one of geographical unity and has a total land area of one-sixth of the whole of Ireland. Some 264 species have been recorded for the six-county area of which about a score are rarities of American origin. It is bounded on the north and east by a seaboard of some 245 miles which includes five great sea loughs and a number of coastal islands. In this area is found every type of marine habitat from the high cliffs of Rathlin and especially Doonmore with its Guillemot population in the region of 10,000 birds, to the low-lying sandy ridges and shingly beaches of Strangford and Carlingford Loughs. With the exception of the Black Guillemot, the auk family is confined to Antrim where they are plentiful, though the Puffin has become reduced in numbers in recent years. The Fulmar was first found nesting in Northern Ireland on Rathlin Island. It soon spread to the mainland cliffs and now breeds inland along the mountain range of Binevenagh in Derry.

Over the last half-century the larger gulls have increased greatly as breeding birds, nowhere more than in Strangford Lough. The Black-headed Gull has developed extensive colonies in this lough and is gradually ousting the terns, four species of which breed on the shingle ridges.

Myxomatosis in 1954 effectively hemmed in the Buzzard which

had begun breeding around the north coast in 1949, and before the disease reached Rathlin Island five pairs of Buzzards made it their home.

The sea loughs with their wide estuaries attract great numbers of wildfowl and waders in winter together with scattered numbers of Red-throated and Great Northern Divers and great rafts of, Common Scoters wintered annually until 1964 off the Down coast. When the north slobs of Strangford Lough become uncovered numbers of waders such as Knot, Dunlin and Bar-tailed Godwit scatter over the surface and on December 1st 1958 an estimated 17,000 Knots were seen on the Down coast. Brent Geese have in recent years greatly regained their numbers. Over 3,000 may be seen spread over the mudflats, chiefly at the north end of the lough. After Christmas the birds decrease rapidly and go elsewhere. The north shore of Belfast Lough and its marshes near Duncrue Street in Belfast has given many remarkable records in recent years: Buff-breasted Sandpiper, Pectoral Sandpiper and Temminck's Stint, have all been seen there. Development has robbed this area of much that was of interest.

In south-east Down lies the massive Mourne range which contains a dozen peaks over 2,000 feet but it is insufficient to support an alpine fauna to any great extent. There are about a dozen pairs of Ring Ouzels and a smaller number of Merlins, but the three or four pairs of Peregrines have decreased, perhaps due to chemical poisoning.

Much of the lower slopes of the Mournes have been clothed with conifers and this has increased the number of passerines there. The Jay has spread rapidly and some thirty pairs inhabit Tollymore Park, with lesser numbers at Mourne Park and Rostrevor. Ravens, too, seem to have increased and there is at least one report of a pair nesting in a tree since 1959. A strange ecological niche is the presence on the forest stands of Grasshopper and Willow Warblers and Meadow Pipits amongst trees up to ten years old.

The Antrim plateau is richer in species than the Mourne area because peat-covered hills are broken by deeply wooded glens opening towards the north-east and the coast. Here Curlew, Golden Plover, Wheatear and Peregrine can be heard together and Common Sandpipers and Dippers haunt the mountain streams. Around the lakes pock-marked in the peat Dunlin and Black-headed Gulls breed and in the glens Hooded Crows, Willow

Warblers and Whitethroats consort together. The Sperrin range joining Derry and Tyrone is equally well supported, because the high grounds which join the west and south sides are deeply trenched and furrowed into long, narrow gorges. Up on the moorland the Merlin and Red Grouse breed.

Intensive agricultural occupation in the eastern counties has reduced the deciduous woodlands almost to extinction and carpets of bluebells and primroses on the slopes of the uplands are evidence of the field-layer of vanished woodland. Though traces of parkland still exist and there are a few well-wooded valleys, they are insufficient to contain any marked woodland species other than Treecreepers and Goldcrests, though very locally Blackcaps are found and Redstarts breed irregularly. Even warblers, which haunt the woodland fringe, are few in number. The limited amount of beechwood means that the Chiffchaff is more restricted in Northern Ireland than the Willow Warbler, which has a wide distribution.

Perhaps the most noticeable natural feature of Northern Ireland is the abundance of reed-fringed lakes in all counties, the great inland sea of Lough Neagh and the wooded islands of Lough Erne in Fermanagh. This means that the north-east is especially rich in water birds. Of the forty-one odd species of anserine birds on the British List, thirty-five species have occurred in the north-east.

Lough Neagh, the largest area of inland water in these islands, is the feeding place of many wildfowl in winter and the breeding site of others. Counts in winter of nearly 22,000 Tufted Ducks, 8,000 Pochard and 4,000 Goldeneye have been reported here. In the nesting season Lough Neagh contains probably the greatest breeding numbers of Great Crested Grebes in Ireland, though since 1959 their numbers have become reduced because of the lowering of the water level. In one reed bed some 50 yards wide and 60 yards long 104 nests were found in 1960 with up to eleven eggs in each. It will be some time before the new growth allows the grebes to spread around the lough again. The Yellow Wagtail has long deserted this area, but in recent years some have bred on reclaimed land in Belfast Lough. Not only has *M. f. flavissima* done so but two pairs of Grey-headed Wagtails did so one year.

Just a mile north of Lough Neagh the River Bann widens out to form Lough Beg, a shallow sheet of water three miles long. The most interesting area is the wetlands on the west or Derry side. Much of it becomes inundated with water during winter and there are a number of permanent pools. The largest water, known locally as Oystercatcher pool, is a favourite feeding area for waders on migration and it is here that species such as Dowitcher, Yellowlegs, White-rumped, Buff-breasted and Broad-billed Sandpipers have been seen. The duck population in winter is enormous. Wigeon can number 2,000, Pintail 600, Tufted Duck over 2,000, Pochard over 2,000. In winter six predatory species have been seen, including a Goshawk. Round the edge of the lake Herons and Rooks breed.

The southern shore is a mass of sand pits, some water-filled, and the area is well covered with reeds, brambles and coarse grass. This is a favourite haunt of many passerines and in the breeding season Black-headed Gulls and Common Terns nest. A pair of Tree Sparrows bred in 1964 for the first time, nesting in trees as they now do in two other localities in Northern Ireland. Altogether 150 species have been recorded in this area.

The Erne lakes contain a maze of wooded islands of importance not only for ducks but for warblers. The Common Scoter breeds there and the Garden Warbler nests freely around the lake. The largest known heronry in Northern Ireland is of thirty nests on Upper Lough Erne. For many years Lesser Black-backed Gulls have bred amongst the trees on Gay Island, Lower Lough Erne.

Whilst some species such as Goldfinch, Bullfinch and Ireland's most recent resident, the Collared Dove, have increased, others are decreasing. The Corncrake has become rare over much of the eastern counties because of the mechanisation of the farms and cutting for silage. This, too, affects the Skylark and Lapwing and there seems to be a general reduction in the number of Snipe in Northern Ireland as the wetlands are being drained: that haunt of geese, the Downpatrick marshes, has ceased to be attractive to wildfowl. More and more bird habitats are being utilised by man and more and more the birds are being pushed from the countryside.

SOME WEXFORD BIRD HAUNTS

Ornithologically Wexford is probably the most interesting county in Ireland. Nearly all our resident species may be found there at some period of the year and the majority breed. The county can also boast of a goodly quota of vagrants.

The county is fairly well wooded and though the natural woods are not very large they are plentiful, and in the many ravines there is a wealth of scrub and bushes bordering the streams. The broad open valleys of the rivers have scattered trees and copses. In these places, and if we include the moors farther inland, there is a fine variety of common species. In summer the woods and bushy places ring with songs of Chiffchaffs and Willow Warblers; the thickets with the song of Whitethroats. The Garden Warbler, Blackcap, Lesser Whitethroat and Redstart are, however, missing.

Afforestation is extensive and the trees vary greatly in age, but seem to have little attraction for species other than Coal Tits and Goldcrests and the younger plantations for Stonechats and Meadow Pipits.

Fine reed beds that stretch far up the River Slaney should hold Bitterns but no longer do so. Near its mouth, on the Slobs and especially in Wexford Harbour, with its masses of waders, Black-tailed Godwits in their hundreds are seen in spring and autumn; a fine sight as they feed or wheel about, seen to advantage at close range.

The Wexford Slobs cover about 6,000 acres. Some picture them as muddy expanses with solid ground intermixed. In reality the Slobs are reclaimed land behind a great sea wall and crossed by broad drainage channels. The large open fields of up to seventy acres or more are bounded by deep ditches and high banks. Once the whole was pasture and on it lay pools and plashy places beloved by geese. Much has now been put under the plough for grain production, but enough grassland remains to support several thousand White-fronted Geese and about seventy Barnacles.

It is an unforgettable experience to walk almost among the geese, the air filled with the calls of flocks moving leisurely from field to field.

Six species are known to have occurred, but nowadays only the two mentioned above and one or two Pink-footed Geese are regular. Of geese the Snow and 'Lesser' Canada are the rarest. Other American visitors known to have visited the North Slob are: Black Duck, Upland Plover, Dowitcher and Pectoral Sandpipers.

A variety of both dabbling and diving ducks float in rafts on the broader channels—Mallard, Teal, Wigeon, Pintail, Shoveler, Scaup, Tufted Duck, Pochard, some Goldeneye and Red-breasted Mergansers.

In autumn waders, common and less common, frequent the channel-edges. Here Spotted Redshanks (some remaining in winter) and Ruffs find one of their favourite Irish haunts.

Slavonian Grebes frequent the channels and the harbour outside the sea wall, where hundreds of Scaup lie scattered over the water and the eye may be drawn to the mud-banks by the voice of Brent Geese, which the telescope shows to number about a thousand.

A bleak place in winter; how different when the Skylarks and Meadow Pipits sing over the extensive pastures and fields of grain in summer! Otherwise few species breed; a few Teal and Sedge Warblers. Yellow Wagtails do not come to use the ideal-looking terrain, nor does the Redshank breed.

Wheatears, Whinchats, White Wagtails dally awhile when on spring and autumn migration and occasionally a Short-toed Lark in October.

Lady's Island Lake and Tacumshin Lake are large lagoons of rather differing character. At the former, two corners, when the water level is suitable, are most attractive to waders—Ruffs, Little Stints, Curlew, Sandpipers and many Dunlin are frequent there on passage in autumn, and most of the other common species. It is a shallow lake and at times a Little Gull or one or more Black Terns are seen in agile flight over its waters.

Tacumshin is shallow and much frequented by waders, to be seen in whirling masses if one wades out to the dry spots known as 'the patches'. Here the variety of waders in autumn and winter includes Grey Plover, Bar-tailed Godwits and, as in the other places, Greenshanks, even in winter.

It was here that in 1938 a pair of Avocets bred, but not again: the variation in water level is not suitable to them. Sandwich and Little Terns nest irregularly. In late winter, perhaps when feeding is running short in Wexford Harbour, up to 200 Brent Geese appear.

The Cull and Bannow Bay have extensive mudflats where many Wigeon, Shelduck in hundreds and numerous waders of all the commoner species occur even in winter. Spotted Redshanks favour the Cull and some 200 Brent Geese frequent Bannow Bay.

Saltee is well known for the migration to be observed there. Hordes of birds make it their first landfall in spring and are even more numerous in autumn. Most are passerines and on some days the cover, which is excessive, swarms with them.

On some days weather conditions force thousands of birds to fly low across the island; Starlings, for instance; or Chaffinches so dense that to put out a hand would seem a simple way to capture some, and having done so find that they are representatives of the race *F. c. hortensis.*

Saltee is not a 'fierce' island; its cliffs are relatively low. They are densely packed with breeding auks, Kittiwakes, some Fulmars, Shags and a thriving little colony of Gannets. All day and night the three species of large gulls keep up a chorus at their nesting sites and the nights are full of the cries of Manx Shearwaters.

The island has much cover of bracken and brambles, though there are good open spaces. It needs hard work to get the best results.

Good migration can also be witnessed from bleak Carnsore Point, when in autumn there is a heavy movement of passerines flying purposefully as they coast in a continuous stream. Beyond them strings of Manx Shearwaters and terns may be moving and with them perhaps one or more of the larger shearwaters or Arctic Skuas.

In this area are new settlements of Tree Sparrows. They build exclusively in gaunt, exposed ruins and always within sight of the sea.

KERRY—WEST AND NORTH-WEST

FRANK KING

The coastal terrain in west and north-west Kerry varies from quiet sand or shingle beaches where the Ringed Plover nests to the great Peregrine cliffs that drop sheer into the Atlantic Ocean where the cries of the Choughs, soaring in the updraught, mingle with the thunder of the surf far below. In between these two extremes there are miles of mudflats that attract hordes of wildfowl and waders during much of the year.

Away from the coast, the northern part of the county is more or less flat, rich farmland with occasional hills of heather and bog-land that rise like brown islands in a green sea. The south is rugged and picturesque with range upon range of high mountains, many of them having large areas of old, deciduous woodland. Between the mountain ranges are fertile river valleys where a lush growth of native and other trees flourishes in the mild climate. Australian Tree Ferns grow in the open air and it is not surprising that in such conditions so fragile a warbler as the Chiffchaff may stay to winter. The whole county has a tremendous importance as a winter refuge for many species of birds.

Seabirds nest on most of the mainland cliffs, but never in any great numbers and one has to go to the offshore islands to find breeding Kittiwakes and Puffins. The great bird haunts therefore are the islands with their gulls, petrels, shearwaters and auks, and the mudflats and marshes that attract large numbers of waders, ducks and Brent Geese.

Immediately to the south of Kerry Head lies the great sweep of Ballyheigue Bay with its strand bordered all the way by sand dunes. Just inside these dunes, in a setting of marsh and reed bed as flat as Holland, is one of the most remarkable bird haunts in the county, Akeagh Lough. This shallow, mud-bottomed lough is especially attractive to water-birds as it is the only permanent stretch of fresh water in all North Kerry. Covering no more than six or seven acres when at its normal level, it is liable to flooding during winter rains, particularly after storms that block the outflow with sand and seaweed. On the other hand, it may dry up almost completely in summer.

As a haunt of duck the lough is chiefly distinguished by the fact that the largest concentration in Ireland of wintering Gadwall is to be found there, and it is a wonderful sight to see a flock of perhaps over a hundred of these comparatively rare duck rise and wheel again and again over the lough and then drop down on to the water with a great flashing of white specula.

During times of flood the numbers and variety of duck increase and there is always the possibility of a North American visitor, such as the Green-winged Teal, which has been recorded there several times. However, the great fame of Akeagh Lough as a haunt of interesting birds lies in the number of unusual waders that it attracts. Its shallowness, its muddy edges with large areas of short, half-submerged grass so beloved of Ruffs, its location in quiet and undisturbed rural surroundings and on the main route of birds migrating along the west coast or following the Shannon valley, all these factors tend to lead to a concentration of waders, especially in the autumn, and being so far west, it also attracts more than its fair share of American waders ranging from the Pectoral Sandpiper, an annual visitor to the lough, to the Western Sandpiper, one of the few individuals of this species ever recorded in Europe. The lough stands on private property and the shooting is also privately owned.

To the south of Ballyheigue Bay lies Barrow Harbour with extensive mudflats with their *Zostera* beds which attract flocks of Brent Geese and herds of Mute and Whooper Swans. It is a quiet and shallow inlet with a sheltered entrance and for much of each day the mudflats are uncovered and hold many waders and duck, especially Wigeon.

The Brent of Barrow Harbour are equally at home in Tralee Bay where about 3,000 frequent the *Zostera* beds that stretch for miles. This bay varies from mudflat along the southern shore as far west as Derrymore Island and the great sandy strands and rocky beaches farther west to shingle on the north shore.

Farther west again lies Brandon Bay with its lip of sand dunes. This bay is a never-failing attraction for skuas, possibly because of the terns that frequent the inshore waters. Here, also, the Common Gull breeds. Overshadowing all is mighty Brandon with its cliffs and corries, its Peregrines and Red Grouse. Still farther west are the Blasket Islands which are the most westerly on the Continental Shelf. All are rich in marine birdlife.

On the southern side of the Dingle Peninsula with its ridge of high mountains are Dingle Bay and Castlemaine Harbour, separated from each other by two sandy peninsulas pointing at each other from opposite shores, the former bay being surprisingly shallow for one that faces directly on to the open Atlantic. It is entirely lacking in mudflats and attracts numbers of scoters at all times of the year. Castlemaine Harbour is an area of quiet mudflats at low tide. Large numbers of duck, chiefly Wigeon, and Brent Geese frequent the flats and great flocks of waders follow the retreating tide-line.

Thus, Kerry occupies an exceptional position with regard to birdlife in Ireland and this is due not only to its favourable climate but also to the great variety and range of suitable habitats and the largely, as yet, unspoiled nature of the countryside.

A SURVEY OF BIRD HAUNTS IN CONNACHT

The province of Connacht is large, consisting of the counties Galway, Mayo, Roscommon, Sligo and Leitrim.

The terrain is extremely diversified and only a brief description of some more important haunts and their birds is possible.

The bird population of woodland and field is less than in eastern counties and becomes thinner as one moves westwards. Woodlands are not extensive, except where afforestation has taken place. There are large areas of rough ground and scrub. In valleys where alder and birch are plentiful Lesser Redpolls are common as they are in some of the older conifer woods, where Siskins breed and which at times are invaded by many Crossbills.

The vast tracts of bog, moorland and mountain are poor in bird life, Skylarks, Meadow Pipits, Hooded Crows and a few Merlins and Golden Plover being about the sole summer inhabitants. In winter scattered flocks of White-fronted Geese are almost the only occupants.

The coasts and islands, where precipitous, have a teeming population of cliff-breeding species. To stand on the awesome cliffs of north Mayo and watch the whirring mass of auks flying to and fro and gliding Fulmars is unforgettable. Locally Choughs enliven the scene.

As elsewhere in Ireland, Tree Sparrows elect to breed in ruins, preferably large, dotted along the very coastline.

The low-lying shores in Sligo, Killala, Blacksod, Clew and Galway Bays have both muddy and sandy stretches suited to numerous waders, both on migration and in winter, and gulls. There is good shelter for divers, but grebes are scarce. Only in Sligo and Killala Bays is there a worthwhile winter population of Common Scoters. In Sligo Bay many Brent Geese may be seen feeding on the muddy expanses.

Barnacle Geese have their stronghold and are now protected on Inishkea off the wild Mullet Peninsula in Co. Mayo. Parties visit the mainland and adjacent islands. To see flocks on the ground or in flight when they fly calling as they return to Inishkea into a westering sun is a remarkable experience.

Off the Mullet several low islands have Storm Petrel colonies. On one the birds are so numerous that, at night, the ground reverberates with their calls and madly flying birds are apt to strike into one. All night, breeding Oystercatchers pipe ceaselessly; in daytime little parties of non-breeding Turnstones may be seen busily feeding along the tide-line and Arctic Terns call overhead. Common Gulls nest on some of the islands and Common Terns on the Mullet, where Dunlin also breed. On Inishmurray, Co. Sligo, there is a large Arctic Tern colony and a few Eiders breed.

Turloughs are a feature in several counties. Rahasane is typical and is nowadays probably one of the most prolific in bird life. It covers an area of about 300 acres. In autumn it consists of short grass with scattered pools. Around these and in soggy places waders abound: Black-tailed Godwits, many still retaining partial summer plumage, Redshanks, Dunlin in hundreds, a few Curlew Sandpipers, the odd Ruff; perhaps something unusual, for Dowitchers have been seen.

As winter approaches the rising water (as at all turloughs) covers most of the flat expanse and the duck then increase. The banks become covered with grazing Wigeon, a thousand or more. Pintail, Shoveler, Teal, Pochard are all in hundreds, other species less. On islands of short grass just above water-level White-fronted Geese graze contentedly, well out of gun-shot; others rest and preen or swim around. Whooper Swans, chiefly in 'chatty' family parties, are scattered over the water, totalling 100 birds or more. From the distance comes a romantic sound as of far-off cattle bells: towards the far end of the turlough one sees a white mass—closely packed Bewick's Swans in number anything between one and three hundred.

In spring the water recedes, the waders return and vast numbers of Golden Plover assemble. When in their thousands they take flight, the air becomes alive with their wonderful trilling 'teeoriar'. If disturbed, perhaps by a Peregrine, they, duck and other waders fill the sky while hundreds of Coots patter over the water. In spring waders are less numerous than in autumn, but March is a wonderful month at a turlough, due to the quantities and variety of duck that halt awhile, and all around in the scrub the Chiffchaffs sing;

but on the turloughs nothing breeds and cattle roam the dry area of short grass until the water and the birds return in autumn.

In Connacht about 190,000 acres are under water. Impressive is the line of lakes southward from Lough Conn. All vary greatly in depth; all have numerous islands both wooded, scrub covered or relatively bare. The coasts are similar. Tufted Duck and Red-breasted Mergansers breed numerously and some Great Crested Grebes. The woods hold nothing but common species. In summer they are alive with Chiffchaffs and Willow Warblers, the reed beds with Sedge Warblers and Reed Buntings. On some islands there are heronries.

Black-headed Gulls at their large colonies have so accentuated the growth of herbage that Common and Arctic Terns have nearly all gone and Common Gull colonies have been adversely affected.

Lesser Black-backed Gulls breed in strength on rocky islands and with them a few Herring Gulls.

Sandwich Terns breed plentifully on flat islands in Lough Conn; this fine tern has colonies on other lakes and on the coastal islands.

Part of the Shannon valley borders Connacht, Lough Ree being rather similar to the western lakes. On its wooded promontories and islands, however, the Garden Warbler breeds commonly, as it does in similar habitat on Lough Key. Grasshopper Warblers are abundant in some of the extensive reed beds.

Drainage in recent years has ruined several splendid wildfowl haunts and the former breeding places of the Black-necked Grebe. But there remain extensive marshy areas where in spring the wonderful bubbling call of the Curlew is heard and at nights the eerie cries of Water Rails. In many places, especially the islands and small holdings of the far west, the nights still vibrate with the Corncrake's voice.

Note. It must be emphasised that many of the places mentioned in the foregoing essays are private property, for instance the Wexford Slobs, Akeagh Lough, Lough Beg, and that permission to visit them must be sought.

THE WILDFOWL SITUATION IN IRELAND

ROBERT F. RUTTLEDGE

Due to paucity of observers it has been impossible, so far, to make any widespread counts of wild duck that breed or winter in Ireland. The task is a great one and the number of localities holding duck is large. Geese, on the other hand, have been fairly accurately counted.

The following observations on duck are the results of impressions, supported in a number of cases by random counts. The general situation as given would, however, appear to be reasonably accurate.

Dabbling Ducks

Of these the only one that breeds in substantial numbers is the Mallard (*Anas platyrhynchos*). There are indications that its success in breeding is falling off, due in great part to the predatory habits of the ever-increasing Hooded Crow (*Corvus cornix*); also to human disturbance and to drainage. There is some indication of decreased numbers in the wintering population. Teal (*Anas crecca*), of which there is a scattered breeding population, are to be found in their thousands in winter, with no evidence of decrease. The wintering stock comes from Iceland, the Continent and Britain. Numbers of Garganey (*Anas querquedula*) are always very small, but perhaps there is a small increase in the past few years. Gadwall (*Anas strepera*) breed in negligible numbers, but are found locally quite often (at Akeagh Lough in Co. Kerry numbers up to 250 or over are almost annual at times of passage) in numbers up to fifty. There is a small residue in winter. Birds come from Iceland. Wigeon (*Anas penelope*) are far the most abundant wintering duck. Breeding in negligible numbers, vast numbers come chiefly from Iceland, and on favoured waters thousands may be found. Tidal waters and estuaries are much resorted to, but during the past twenty to thirty years increasingly large numbers are found on flooded areas inland. Pintail (*Anas acuta*), a negligible breeding species, is found locally in winter and more especially on passage, in flocks of 300 or over, and there undoubtedly has been an increase since about 1930. Most come from Iceland. Shoveler (*Spatula clypeata*) have increased and spread as a breeding species since the beginning of the century. Nowadays assemblies of 200 to 500 birds are not unusual locally, chiefly in March and April.

Diving Ducks

Scaup (*Aythya marila*) come increasingly to winter and gatherings of 2,000 to 3,000 in certain favoured haunts are regular nowadays. The source of most is chiefly Iceland. Tufted Duck (*Aythya fuligula*) have greatly increased as a breeding species and the increase may well be continuing. Wintering birds, which are numerous, come in the main from Iceland. Pochard (*Aythya ferina*) breed spasmodically in one or two places, but the numbers on passage and in winter are considerable and show a marked increase in recent years. Goldeneye (*Bucephala clangula*) do not breed, but as winter visitors are widely distributed on inland waters (2,800 have been counted on Lough Neagh) and on estuaries locally in flocks totalling many hundreds of birds.

Sea Ducks

Long-tailed Duck (*Clangula hyemalis*) appear in fluctuating numbers but seldom in flocks that exceed thirty individuals. The north-west coast is most frequented. The origin of our birds is unknown. Common Scoter (*Melanitta nigra*): there is a small, almost static, breeding population (less than 100 pairs) and a large wintering one, the origin of the latter being uncertain. Flocks often number 1,000 or more individuals. Eider (*Somateria mollissima*): very slowly expanding breeding population. Numbers do not seem to be augmented in winter.

Sawbill

The Red-breasted Merganser (*Mergus serrator*) is a common and widespread breeding bird, not decreasing. Flocks of up to fifty birds are found on tidal waters in winter.

Shelduck

(*Tadorna tadorna.*) No evidence of decrease, more likely the reverse. Flocks of 200 to 300 are not infrequent on the east coast; occasionally over 500 are seen in a flock. Widespread as a breeding bird on coasts.

GENERAL

It will be noticed how greatly dependent on Iceland we are for our wintering populations. Since so many wildfowl come from there to find in Ireland their chief wintering haunts, it is incumbent on us to keep sufficient haunts available for them if we are to expect their continued presence.

Drainage in some areas has seriously affected many of the haunts of dabbling ducks and also diving ducks. There still seem to be sufficient haunts, but for how long? The turloughs (winter lakes of shallow water, only a few inches in depth) are a much favoured habitat for dabbling ducks, geese and swans, and so far not very many have been drained. Diving ducks resort to the large lakes which are deeper and are little affected adversely.

Geese

Greylag (*Anser anser*). Once a locally common goose. In 1946, 6,000 or more could be found on the Wexford Slobs. By 1954 the number had dropped to under 200 and by 1960 if even one was seen it would be a notable event. A similar decrease has taken place in other haunts and it is probable that less than 1,000 winter in Ireland. This decrease is strange and the more difficult to explain since there has been recently a marked increase in Iceland, whence our wintering Greylags came. The White-fronted Goose (*Anser albifrons flavirostris*) is *the* goose of Ireland. There is a wintering population of at least 9,000. The greatest concentration is on the Wexford Slobs, but here there is a slight decrease due to tillage activities and the drainage accompanying. Several haunts, especially in Connacht, have been deserted due to complete drainage of marshes in the past three years.

Brent Geese (*Branta b. hrota*) show a healthy state, perhaps some recent increase. The wintering total is between 11,000 and 12,000. Barnacle Geese (*Branta leucopsis*) come from the Greenland breeding grounds. Our population seems fairly static at about 4,000 birds.

Swans

Mute Swan (*Cygnus olor*). Widespread as a breeding bird. Has increased in number and size of flocks tremendously during the past ten years. The Whooper Swan (*Cygnus cygnus*) was always locally well established in winter. Since 1942 it has increased and spread greatly. This ties in with the great and sudden increase of the bird in Iceland. Herds of 150 are not uncommon, though usually it is in much smaller flocks that are very widespread. Western Ireland and one or two places in the north of the country are the chief haunts and in the west the turloughs are the favoured habitat. It has in many places replaced Bewick's Swan (*Cygnus bewickii*) which formerly exceeded it in numbers. There is some evidence of an increase of Bewick's and locally up to 300 may be seen on turloughs or other flooded areas. All three species of swans usually avoid the deeper waters of Ireland.

It would appear then that, with the notable exception of the Greylag Goose and perhaps on a small scale the White-fronted Goose (which may perhaps have redistributed itself) and a reduction in Mallard, our wildfowl show no decrease, indeed the reverse. Many of the diving duck species are not much sought by hunters and our sea ducks not at all.

We must, however, be very alive to the dangers of habitat ruination by draining, agricultural development, disturbance by speedboats and so on. Now is the time to act so that the chances for the sport and pleasure we enjoy may be perpetuated.

MIGRATION

A GENERAL SURVEY

Barrington (1900) over the years 1881–97 amassed a vast amount of data concerning migration, collected from the light-keepers around our coast. His book analyses these data and gives much detail extracted from the reports he received. It was an invaluable task, but it was subject to limitations.

Often there was no lightkeeper who was a capable observer present on an (ornithologically) important light-station; if there was, the chances were great that he was on 'shore-liberty' or off duty when important happenings were taking place. At best his scope, in limited spare time, was confined to those nights when conditions drew birds to the lantern; at all times, in most cases, his ground was limited and lacking in cover and other amenities that attract passing birds.

From time to time others have followed in Barrington's foot-steps with enquiries on a more limited scale. Professor C. J. Patten made visits to some of the more important light-stations. Here again, although he collected invaluable data, he was limited by constricted space.

Certainly the bird casualties at lights often included rarities, or what were then believed to be rarities by the very nature of the shortcomings of haphazard noting. Eagle Clarke (1912) has written of certain phenomena as they affected Ireland and Witherby *et al.* (1938) give statements and conclusions based on the above mentioned works and of the works of the British Association Committee.

A study of Barrington (1900) leaves one with the impression that passage migration was not then appreciated. It is too often apparent that immigration was considered to be taking place when in fact the birds were passage migrants.

The frequent reports of birds heading for the mainland following a night when they were abundant at the lantern can surely be attributed in most cases to the attraction of land for tired birds as dawn replaced the effect of the lantern glare. There was, of course, at times heavy immigration in spring and autumn.

Under many species in the Systematic List some information of their migrations, times of arrival and departure and nature of the movements is given.

A great deal has been learnt during the past fourteen years and the knowledge continues to accumulate. Much of this derives from the establishment of Bird Observatories. In these we have places manned for continuous periods, by people there for the sole purpose of migration study—a very different proposition from the case of the lightkeepers who had helped so willingly.

Up to the time of the establishment of Great Saltee as an observatory both the Pied Flycatcher and Tree Pipit were considered scarce and rare vagrants respectively. This belief was soon exploded.

Rare birds have been found to be in reality less rare and a number of species have been reported for the first time in Ireland.

Even before 1900 it was well known that migration, whatever its type, was heaviest on the Co. Wexford coast. For the study of this Great Saltee has catered admirably. The observatory on John's Island in the Copeland Islands group off Co. Down has pictured the migration at that corner of Ireland. Tory Island Observatory has added greatly to knowledge of migration in the north-west with its obvious connection with Greenland/Iceland birds. Cape Clear receives annually a number of birds rarely, if ever before, seen in Ireland, but it normally lacks the great weight of passerine migration that passes through Saltee.

Besides these established observatories there have been others of a temporary nature and they have filled a useful role. Great Saltee has now been closed but the opening of an observatory at Malin Head, Co. Donegal, promises to be of extreme importance.

There are several types of migration in Ireland, all of the usual forms found elsewhere: spring immigrants that will remain in summer and will nest. The majority of these are passerines that arrive on our south-east coast. These birds emigrate after the breeding season, again using the south-east and south coasts as departure points.

Most are birds of southern origin and among the first to arrive are Lesser Black-backed Gulls, Sandwich Terns and Wheatears. Then *hirundines* and warblers begin to pour in. Whinchats, Redstarts, come in small numbers but Spotted Flycatchers are often plentiful.

In autumn the south-east and part of the east coast experience waves of immigrant winter visitors.

Blackbirds and Chaffinches from Europe arrive often in hundreds per day; Fieldfares, Redwings, Black Redstarts, Pied Flycatchers, Starlings are amongst the many species arriving and/or passing.

Autumn is the time too when the Co. Donegal stations witness the arrival of visitors from the north-west—Golden Plover, Water Rails, Wheatears, Meadow Pipits, Lapland Buntings, to mention a few. Copeland also experiences the arrival of winter visitors.

Like Saltee, Cape Clear is even more dependent on anticyclonic winds to bring birds up from Iberia and even from the Mediterranean regions, but it seems to act as a magnet for accidentals from almost anywhere in Europe.

In south-east Ireland in September and October a great build-up of migrants occurs along the coast. Eventually many fly out over the sea heading southward until lost to view. At the same time a heavy coasting movement is often in progress. Swallows stream down the east coast, many peeling off at Carnsore Point to continue in a southerly direction over the sea. Many turn westward along the coast and this stream is augmented by overland migrants. At each southward projecting headland a proportion break away southward over the sea. In this remarkable movement Skylarks, *hirundines*, Meadow Pipits, White Wagtails and Linnets participate.

It is noticeable that Whimbrels, though they travel along the east coast in spring and autumn, are far more numerous on the west coast. The White Wagtail is more frequent in spring than in autumn on the west coast; in autumn its migration is heavier on the east than on the west coast.

Winter visitors arrive on all coasts, but again more heavily in the east. On that coast the majority are birds of Continental origin; birds from the north-west and north make their landfall on the north and north-west coasts.

Passage migration is a feature of all coasts. It is at all times most in evidence on the east side and at the south-east corner of Ireland and least along our west coast where the volume is greatly dependent on meteorological conditions.

Spring passage is easily detected, not only on the coasts but inland. On the coasts species pass that do not breed in Ireland or only in very small numbers. Thus the Redstarts, Tree Pipits and Pied Flycatchers are probably northbound passage migrants. Inland, duck of several species pass through in March. Black Terns make use of the inland waterways.

The reverse movement that occurs in autumn is sometimes very spectacular and usually more heavy than in spring. Skylarks are abundant in October. They pass through the country on a wide front. They are seen arriving on the northern coasts and departing southward over the sea in great numbers from the Wexford coast. These movements tie in very satisfactorily. The same occurs in the case of the Meadow Pipit.

Lapland Buntings, for which species there is no evidence of regular wintering in Ireland, are notable migrants on the west coast, more so in autumn than in spring.

What the west coast lacks in numbers and variety of migrating passerines it makes up for in the interesting volume of sea-bird migration, both in spring and autumn.

In recent years it has been adequately shown that, apart from a stream of passing Manx Shearwaters, Fulmars, Gannets and auks, birds that were little known before are also regular on passage: Great Shearwaters, Sooty Shearwaters, a few Cory's Shearwaters, Great Skuas, Pomarine Skuas.

Off Cape Clear also these species are regular, sometimes in great numbers, and also the Balearic Shearwater.

There is only a mere trickle of these larger shearwaters through the Irish Sea. In spring the sea-bird passage is less marked.

The chain of waterways provided by the Shannon valley and the line of large Connacht lakes, both lying north-south, seem favoured as fly-lines by several species, particularly in autumn. Golden Plover, Ringed Plover, Dunlin, Black-tailed Godwits, Turnstones are all regular, Grey Plover, Knots, Sanderlings, Arctic Skuas and Black Terns less regularly. Similarly the Bann estuary and that river south to Loughs Beg and Neagh have an appeal for migrating waterfowl and waders and also some passerines.

Vagrants from Europe arrived at any point, but most often they are noticed on the Cos. Wexford and Cork coasts. Those from America are most often detected in Co. Kerry, but they have been seen in north-east Ireland, and in eastern coastal counties.

There are local movements, weather movements and those of dispersal within the country.

References

BARRINGTON, R. M. (1900): *Migration of Birds at Irish Light Stations.* London and Dublin.

CLARKE, W. EAGLE (1912): *Studies in Bird Migration.* London and Edinburgh.

WITHERBY, H. F. *et al.* (1938): *The Handbook of British Birds.* London.

SYSTEMATIC LIST OF BIRDS

Black-throated Diver: *Gavia arctica*

Scarce winter visitor and passage migrant.

One to three, rarely up to six, are reported each year. Occurrences take place in the months October to May; there are records for July, August and September. It occurs singly as a rule, but seven were seen off the Aran Islands, Co. Galway, in November 1957. Most occurrences take place on the north-east and east coasts, seldom on the west and south. Found normally on tidal waters there have, however, been occurrences inland in Leix, Meath, Roscommon, Galway and on Lough Neagh. Birds in breeding plumage have been seen on several occasions.

The record of breeding in Ireland was erroneous (*Br. Birds*, 43: 167).

Great Northern Diver: *Gavia immer*

Winter visitor. Passage migrant.

Usually found singly or in twos or threes. On every coast there are specially favoured bays where considerable numbers may be seen scattered over the water. Quite exceptional was a compact flock of about sixty birds seen in Dundrum Bay, Co. Down, on December 19th 1964. The Great Northern Diver is found in greatest numbers on the north and west coasts; in the south it is less plentiful than elsewhere. To the larger inland waters this diver is a not infrequent visitor in winter; on some lakes it is of fairly regular occurrence. On occasions, protracted stays on inland waters have been recorded.

Though there are fairly frequent records for September, October is the usual month of arrival and from then until April this bird is plentiful; fewer are seen in May. It has occurred in June, July and August.

Birds in summer plumage are frequent, most often in July and August but also in May.

A large proportion of the birds frequenting our coasts is immature.

Red-throated Diver: *Gavia stellata*

Scarce resident. Passage migrant. Winter visitor.

First found breeding in Co. Donegal in 1884. It has continued to do so and for at least twenty years single pairs have bred in at least two other localities in that county.

This diver is widespread all round our coasts during winter. Most often seen in scattered ones or twos; small flocks are sometimes noticed and as many as thirty together have been reported when migration was in progress.

First arrivals are occasionally seen in September. It is from October, the month of greatest numbers, until April, more rarely to the end of May, that the birds are present on the coasts. Outside the breeding season it is seldom found inland, but has occurred in Offaly, Monaghan, on Lough Derg and on Lough Beg in Derry.

Birds in breeding plumage occur occasionally in spring and autumn, possibly on passage.

Great Crested Grebe: *Podiceps cristatus*

Resident.

As a breeding species it is locally abundant, having greatly increased in numbers and extension of range since the start of the century. Perhaps the greatest breeding density is on Lough Neagh. A census made in the Lough Neagh basin in May 1965 showed over 500 birds present, while on Belfast Lough there were 140 non-breeding birds. It is extremely numerous in Co. Cavan and in the Lough Erne basin where 108 breeding birds were counted in 1965.

In 1945 it was absent or very scarce as a breeding bird south of a line from Dundalk to Limerick. It bred in Co. Wexford in 1946, in Co. Limerick in 1947 (possibly in 1946), in Co. Wicklow in 1951, in Co. Dublin it attempted to breed in 1958 and did so in Co. Meath in 1961.

In western Donegal, where most lakes are unsuited to it, the bird is absent. It has, however, bred near Dunfanaghy and does so on Lough Fern and in the enclosed part of Lough Swilly.

In Connacht west of the great lakes it is not known to breed, nor in west Clare.

In autumn the majority move to tidal waters for the winter, but in the west and south-west it is rare both inland and on tidal waters. It is common near Cork and Cobh and is becoming increasingly so in Wexford Harbour.

Over 260 have been counted in Belfast Lough as early as August 14th in 1957; 265 on September 6th 1953 and 450 on September 8th 1963. Such numbers do not occur elsewhere in Ireland.

A marked passage has been noticed at Lough Beg, Co. Derry, in July and August. Numbers fluctuate along the east coast in spring and autumn.

Red-necked Grebe: *Podiceps griseigena*

Scarce winter visitor.

Before 1953 only fifteen occurrences were known, but probably as a result of more intensive watching, the bird is now recorded almost annually. In most years there are one to three records, in 1956 there were four, in one case of six birds together. Occurrences are usually of single birds, sometimes two or three together.

Again perhaps due to more regular observation, the bays of Co. Dublin and Strangford Lough seem the most favoured haunts. Records are for the counties Kerry (2), Cork (4), Waterford (1), Wexford (2), Wexford or Wicklow (1), Dublin (11 or 12), Down (5), Antrim (1), Down or Antrim (1), Donegal (2), Derry (1), Armagh (1). Occurrences have taken place on or near the coast, rarely inland. There is no record for Connacht. Inland one is said to have been obtained on the River Shannon in February 1865. One was seen at Acton Lake, Co. Armagh, in January 1956 and one at Portavo reservoir, Co. Down, in January 1957.

Where the months are known, occurrences have been in January (11), February (5), March (5), April (3), October (1), November (1), December (6).

The earliest date in autumn is October 30th, the latest in spring April 24th.

Slavonian Grebe: *Podiceps auritus*

Winter visitor. Vagrant in May and June.

Until recently this grebe occurred annually in winter in marine loughs and bays in the north-east and in Dublin Bay, but in the past five years it has less often been reported though in the winter 1963–64 and autumn 1964 more were seen than for some time. It is, however, of annual occurrence in Wexford Harbour and it also frequents the broad channels of the North Slob, Co. Wexford.

On the west coast it is found here and there, most regularly in Killala, Blacksod and Clew Bays. In Co. Galway the few records are from Galway Bay; Ballyvaughan Bay has provided the very few records for Co. Clare and it is doubtfully regular there. It has been recorded from all maritime counties. There are a few reports of it in Co. Kerry: the Slavonian Grebe is rare on the south coast. Individuals have occurred in at least six inland counties, some on waters in the midlands.

Parties of up to six birds are not infrequent; ten or more together have been seen. It appears more numerously in some years than others; in some winters only one or two are reported.

From September onwards occurrences increase: most records are for January, February and March, a few in April. There are reports of it in May and June, none for July or August.

Black-necked Grebe: *Podiceps nigricollis*

Formerly summer resident. Scarce, irregular winter visitor.

The history of the breeding of the Black-necked Grebe has been outlined in *Birds of Ireland* (1954) pp. 9–10.

The first known attempt at breeding was in Achill Island, Co. Mayo, in 1906.

The site where definite breeding was first discovered was, in fact, a turlough near Briarfield in the Castleplunket district of Co. Roscommon. This was the breeding haunt of up to fifteen pairs until the place was completely drained in 1957.

In 1929 the sensational discovery was made that there was a strong colony at Lough Funshinagh, Co. Roscommon. In 1930 the estimated strength was 250 breeding pairs.

Another breeding station, of two or three pairs, was near Tulsk, in the Castleplunket district, and for a number of years up to ten pairs bred at Levally Lough in Co. Galway. Unfavourable conditions at Lough Funshinagh and total drainage of the other sites banished the birds and none has bred since 1957. Isolated and irregular cases of breeding were known in Westmeath and near Enniskillen, Co. Fermanagh. No Black-necked Grebes are now known to breed in Ireland.

There are, in fact, very few waters in Ireland entirely suited to the rather special needs of this species.

Winter occurrences are scarce and irregular and usually of single birds, chiefly on the east coast. Since breeding ceased, the bird is rarely seen in summer; one was reported in Bantry Bay, Co. Cork, on August 20th 1963.

Little Grebe: *Podiceps ruficollis*

Resident. Partial migrant.

As a breeding bird the Little Grebe is generally distributed and is found in every county.

On some favoured waters the breeding population is so great that the bird can be considered as breeding colonially.

It nests on marine islands such as Rathlin and Achill and in recent years on Inishbofin, but not on Clare Island. In Co. Galway its range extends to the western seaboard; it breeds here and there in western Donegal where suitable habitat exists. In western Kerry, where it is at all times rare, breeding was first recorded in 1954.

Although many remain to winter on the larger inland waters, most resort to tidal waters at that season. Thirty to forty have been noticed in August in a compact flock. In October flocks of up to thirty birds are frequent. On the west coast winter flocks of more than twelve individuals are rare.

Casualties occur at light-stations on the south and south-east coasts and the Little Grebe occurs with some regularity at Cape Clear Island, Co. Cork, in September and October. It is not yet clear whether these movements are merely of dispersal or are of further ranging migrants.

Black-browed Albatross: *Diomedea melanophrys*
Two, probably three, records.

One seen off Cape Clear Island, Co. Cork, on September 24th 1963. One seen in Brandon Bay, Co. Kerry, August 15th 1964.

It is virtually certain that an albatross seen off Malin Head, Co. Donegal on September 26th 1963 was an immature bird of this species.

Wilson's Petrel: *Oceanites oceanites*
Two records.

One was shot on Lough Erne, Co. Fermanagh, on October 1st 1891 after a severe storm. The specimen is in the National Museum. One was found dying at Mossvale, Co. Down, on October 2nd 1891.

The wing lengths of these specimens are 148 mm and 159 mm and therefore come within the large Antarctic group of Wilson's Petrel. The Mossvale bird is extremely large and can only be referred to a far southern population; the Lough Erne bird is intermediate in its measurement and is considered to be between birds of the Antarctic and Subantarctic (W. R. P. Bourne).

Leach's Petrel: *Oceanodroma leucorrhoa*
Has bred. Passage migrant. Accidental inland, and in winter.

A very few have bred in the past. Such occurrences were on Inishtearaght and Inishnabro off Co. Kerry and Blackrock off Co. Mayo towards the end of last century. In 1906 about three pairs bred on Duvillaun Beg off Co. Mayo.

Some search of old haunts was made in 1924, followed by intensive search by day and night of all likely islands from Rathlin Island, down the west coast to Skelligs. Without doubt no colony exists. A few pairs probably breed on the Stags of Broadhaven, off Co. Mayo, where in 1946 and 1947 birds were seen and heard. In August 1965 one was captured and it or others seen subsequently in the Storm Petrel colony on Great Skellig, Co. Kerry. No others have been traced but it is possible that, as in the past, cases of breeding continue to be sporadic.

There is regular passage in autumn along the west coast, but very little evidence of movement off the south coast. Occasionally birds pass southward in autumn on the east coast; on September 28th 1952, at least twenty together were seen in Dublin Bay and others were flying south-east.

There is only one spring migration record; it is of a bird caught at Fastnet lighthouse, Co. Cork, on May 5th 1896.

'Wrecks' occurred following the exceptional storms in September and October 1891; even more disastrous was that during October and November 1952. On those occasions birds were found, dead or exhausted, widespread. In many cases they had been swept right across to the eastern counties.

January and December each provide two records.

Madeiran Petrel: *Oceanodroma castro*

One record.

A female was obtained at Blackrock lighthouse, Co. Mayo, on October 18th 1931. The specimen is in the National Museum.

Storm Petrel: *Hydrobates pelagicus*

Summer resident. Occasional in winter.

There are breeding colonies, large and small, on many islands off the west and south-west coasts. The following colonies are known:

Co. Cork. Bull Rock; about 150 pairs in 1955.

Co. Kerry. Great Skellig; 4,000 pairs in 1965. Puffin Island; less than 1,000 pairs in 1955. Inishvickillaun; 7,600 pairs estimated in 1953. Inishtooskert; 3,000 to 5,000 pairs in 1955. Inishnabro; about 1,000 pairs in 1955. Inishtearaght; 'vast numbers' impossible to estimate due to the terrain. Illaunboy and Beginish; a few pairs, 1953.

Co. Clare. Mattle Island and Mutton Island.

Co. Galway. Inishbofin; a few pairs. Inishshark; 'a considerable colony'. High Island; up to 40 pairs in 1943. Corrigeenagowlra off Lettermullen; up to 15 pairs in 1942.

Co. Mayo. Inishglora; well over 1,000 pairs in 1965. Duvillaun Beg; up to 150 pairs in 1942. Inishkeeragh; at least 100 pairs in

1942. Islands supporting colonies of less than 100 pairs are Pig Island, Stags of Broadhaven, Kid Island, Carrickawilt, Duvillaun More, Caher Island, Inishdalla.

The Storm Petrel does not breed in the Aran Islands (Galway) and no longer does so on Blackrock (Mayo).

Co. Donegal. Roaninish; 250 to 350 pairs in 1953, 1955 and 1957. The estimate of about 1,000 pairs made in 1947 was probably excessive. Rathlin O'Birne; the colony is very small. Inishduff; 20 to 30 pairs in 1960. Tory Island; about 20 pairs in 1962. On Inishbeg it has bred and one or two pairs do so on Umfin and Torglass.

None is now known to breed in Rathlin Island, Co. Antrim; in 1956 the colony on Sheep Island had ceased to exist.

A pair bred successfully under a heap of sticks on Tuskar Rock, Co. Wexford, in 1959.

Birds arrive at their colonies about the end of April, more usually in May. Dispersal takes place in September and October; most move farther away in November and December. From January to March the bird is rarely seen.

From time to time severe storms in autumn cause 'wrecks'; the victims are then found strewn all over the country.

Manx Shearwater: *Procellaria puffinus*

Summer visitor. Very scarce in winter. Probable passage migrant in autumn.

The Manx Shearwater, *Procellaria p. puffinus*, breeds on a number of marine islands and a few mainland promontories. The most notable colonies are off the south-west coast. Of these, that on Great Skellig was estimated at 3,000 pairs in 1964. There are 'strong colonies' on Inishtearaght and Inishtooskert but even estimated numbers have been impossible to arrive at. The strength of the colony on Puffin Island, Co. Kerry, was put at between 10,000 and 20,000 pairs in 1955. If this figure is correct, it makes this by far the greatest colony on the Irish coast.

On the Saltees off Co. Wexford there are small colonies. East coast breeding haunts are Bray Head, Lambay, Howth Head, Ireland's Eye and the Copeland Islands. Rathlin Island, Co. Antrim, has a small breeding population.

Of the scattered haunts on the west coast, that on High Island, Co. Galway, is probably the most important.

The Manx Shearwater appears near its breeding haunts in March. Few are seen after October. It has been recorded in February.

Apart from birds that are moving to feeding grounds, it seems probable that there is an appreciable passage along the west coast in autumn.

There are four instances of the bird being found far inland in June (2), July and September.

Two ringed at Copeland off Co. Down were recovered in Wales; two at Skomer, Wales, were found in Down and Antrim. A young bird ringed at Copeland in August 1956 was recovered the following December in Brazil.

Balearic Shearwater: *P. p. mauretanicus*

Regular spring and autumn passage migrant.

This race was first recorded in 1956 when, on August 1st, one was identified in Belfast Lough. It is regularly recorded off Cape Clear, Co. Cork, where, during the years 1961, 1962 and 1963, a total of thirty-three was reported, chiefly in March and April, but several times in August, September and October. It has several times been seen off Great Saltee, Co. Wexford, in September. Off Co. Donegal there are records for April and September. Off Co. Down one was reported in September 1964. One was seen between the Kerry mainland and Great Skellig on June 16th 1963 and two off Brandon Point, Co. Kerry on August 28th 1965.

Little Shearwater: *Procellaria baroli*

Five records.

One came aboard a ship when off the Bull Rock, Co. Cork, on May 6th 1853. The specimen is in the National Museum. Two individuals passed Malin Head, Co. Donegal, within ten minutes of one another on October 22nd 1964. All were referable to the Madeiran form *Procellaria baroli baroli*.

Two Little Shearwaters (race undetermined) were seen together off Brandon Point, Co. Kerry, on August 28th 1965 and one off the Mullet, Co. Mayo, on September 18th 1965.

Great Shearwater: *Procellaria gravis*

Passage migrant chiefly in autumn.

It has long been known that the Great Shearwater was found, sometimes in considerable numbers, off the south and south-west coasts and that on occasions it penetrates St. George's Channel as far as the Waterford coast.

Further study has proved that a few pass Cape Clear, Co. Cork, annually; as many as about 500 were seen there on July 14th 1963. Off the coast of Kerry this shearwater is met with regularly and it has been found to pass down the west coast and along the north coast in autumn. There are a few records of it on the east coast: Dublin Bay (1), off Rosslare, Co. Wexford (1), off Carnsore Point, Co. Wexford (1). Several have been seen off Great Saltee.

On two occasions after gales in August and September 1965 a total of over 11,000 passed Cape Clear and abnormally large numbers passed southwards along the west coast.

Some have been reported off Co. Cork in April, but August and particularly September are the months in which it is most frequent: there are records for May, June, July, October, November and December.

Large shearwaters are often seen off the south and west coasts under conditions which make specific identification impossible; the birds are either of this or the following species.

Cory's Shearwater: *Procellaria diomedea.*

Passage migrant in late summer.

The records of this shearwater off the south coast have been almost annual since its presence was first detected in 1958. Most reports come from Cape Clear, Co. Cork, where, on August 10th 1962, the remarkable total of 157 passed west during 130 minutes. On July 14th 1963, 200 flew west at a time when large numbers of Great Shearwaters were passing. On August 29th 1961, five together were seen off Dunquin, Co. Kerry. Four have been recorded off Great Saltee, Co. Wexford.

Following gales in August and September 1965 many more than usual were seen along the west coast and off the south coast.

Occurrences have been in July, August and September, rarely in October.

Sooty Shearwater: *Procellaria grisea*
Late summer and autumn passage migrant.

There is a movement along the north coast which becomes very marked along the west coast and off the south coast. There is an irregular trickle of southbound birds along the east coast.

Numbers on the south and west coasts vary from year to year, but often reach a large total: 260 have been seen to pass Cape Clear on one day and between September 1st and 15th a total of 1,021 were counted. Large concentrations occur off the south-west coast; a raft of at least 200 has been seen off Dursey Island.

In a period of prolonged passage off Erris Head, Co. Mayo, over 200 were counted on September 3rd.

Greater numbers than hitherto recorded were seen off the north, west and south coasts in August, September and October 1965.

Passage is evident in June (rarely), July, August, September, early October with stragglers into November.

The peak period of passage is at the end of August and early in September.

At Cape Clear there are a few records for April and one for May.

Bulwer's Petrel: *Bulweria bulwerii*
One record.

One was identified off Cape Clear, Co. Cork on August 26th 1965.

Fulmar: *Fulmarus glacialis*
Summer visitor.

Since nesting was first proved in Mayo in 1911, the Fulmar has extended its range apace and now breeds in all maritime counties except Louth, Meath and Leitrim, these having no suitable cliffs.

An outline of the history of the spread of the Fulmar and list of its breeding colonies is given in *Birds of Ireland* (1954).

New sites are constantly being occupied and 'prospecting' continues.

Among new breeding stations are Kerry Head, Brandon Point, Co. Kerry; Power Head, Sheep's Head, Brow Head, Cape Clear, all in Co. Cork; Helvick Head, Co. Waterford; Little Saltee, Co. Wexford; Wicklow Head; Howth Head, and cliffs, near Dalkey, Co. Dublin; Killard Point, Co. Down; White Head, Bohesian Bay, Carrick-a-rede, Co. Antrim; Binevenagh, Co. Derry; Dunaff Head, Co. Donegal. Many places being 'prospected' up to 1954 have no doubt been since occupied.

Fulmars arrive at their breeding stations sometimes, though temporarily, in November, more usually in January.

The 'dark' or 'blue' phase has been identified seventeen times, having been reported at Cape Clear, off Dursey Island, Great Skellig, Kerry Head, Great Saltee and Lambay. One found on the Dublin coast in November 1867 is in the National Museum. Occurrences have taken place in April (4), June (3), July (3), August (3), September (2), November (1).

A Fulmar was seen on Lough Conn, Co. Mayo, on June 17th 1963; this lake is about ten miles from the nearest salt water and much farther from the open sea.

Gannet: *Sula bassana*

Summer visitor. Passage migrant. Not uncommon in winter.

There are three Gannetries: Little Skellig, Co. Kerry, known since about 1700; average strength about 10,000 pairs: Bull Rock, Co. Cork, known since 1853; about 500 pairs: Great Saltee, Co. Wexford; first occupied in 1929 by one pair: the number has increased annually; in 1964 at least 100 pairs were breeding.

There is no satisfactory evidence in support of statements that Gannets bred on the Stags of Broadhaven, Co. Mayo.

There is movement along both the east and west coasts in January in some years, but chiefly in February, March and April. A return migration occurs in October, sometimes in September.

In winter the Gannet is not uncommon.

Young birds ringed at Scottish and Welsh colonies have been recovered off our coasts in autumn and winter. Young ringed at Great Saltee have been found on the coasts of France and Portugal. An interesting case is of one recovered off Tripoli in Libya in the November following its being ringed as a young bird at Saltee.

Occasionally immature birds have occurred far inland in autumn, once in May.

Cormorant: *Phalacrocorax carbo*
Resident. Winter visitor. Partial migrant.

The Cormorant is generally distributed on the coasts, breeding locally in suitable areas. It does not nest in Co. Down and, with the exception of Lambay, where 100 pairs nest, few breed on the east coast. The Lambay colony has decreased considerably during the past thirty years. There are many colonies along the south coast; that on Little Saltee fluctuates in strength between 265 and 320 pairs. Colonies are scattered along the west coast and on marine islands. There are few colonies on the north coast; Rathlin Island is not a breeding station.

There are a few colonies in trees on inland waters. Non-breeding birds flight regularly in summer to roost inland. The Cormorant is found plentifully inland at all seasons.

The majority of our breeding birds are resident or subject to local movements; others migrate to Britain, Spain and Portugal. In addition, there is a movement northward from southern colonies.

An immigration from Scotland takes place in autumn.

Shag: *Phalacrocorax aristotelis*
Resident. Winter visitor.

This species breeds abundantly on precipitous cliffs and marine islands, but much less numerously on the east coast than elsewhere. On the west coast it greatly outnumbers the Cormorant. About 250 pairs breed on Great Saltee, Co. Wexford.

Some come from Scotland to winter off our coasts.

Storm-driven Shags have been found far inland, most often in winter. A Shag was seen in flight at Lough Beg, Co. Derry, in May.

Heron: *Ardea cinerea*
Resident. Partial migrant. Winter visitor.

The Heron is common and widespread, breeding in every county and in the most desolate regions. Herons habitually nest on lake islands in bushes only a few feet high. It still nests on the sea-cliffs at Dingle Harbour, Co. Kerry.

In 1964 a fairly comprehensive census showed that there were at least 213 heronries, the mean number of pairs being 939. In Connacht twenty-two heronries were reported (clearly there are many more), in Leinster fifty-two, Munster eighty-three, Ulster fifty-six.

Heronries of over fifteen nests were at Tongeree, Upper Lough Erne (over 30), Co. Fermanagh; Bellurgan Park (20 to 30), Co. Louth; Castle Grove (27), Co. Donegal; Stuart Hall (27), Co. Tyrone; Isle o'Valla (22), Co. Down; Ballyscullion Wood (21), Co. Derry; Garnish Island near Sneem (20 to 24), Co. Kerry; Woodbrook (about 19), Co. Leix; Inishfree, Lower Lough Erne (18), Co. Fermanagh. There are twelve of between ten and fifteen nests. Three or four nests is the average size of those containing less than ten.

In many cases numbers of birds are much below average due to recent severe winters and the figures given should be taken as being below normal.

Herons in Ireland are largely sedentary, but there is a tendency for young birds to disperse. There is emigration to Scotland. Young birds ringed in Scandinavia, Denmark and France have been found in Ireland in their first winter: winter visitors also come from Scotland and England.

Purple Heron: *Ardea purpurea*

Two records.

A specimen now in the National Museum was obtained at Carrickmacross, Co. Monaghan, previous to 1834. One was seen on Cape Clear Island, Co. Cork, on May 2nd 1965.

Little Egret: *Egretta garzetta*

Vagrant.

Previous to 1940 there was only one authentic record; since then the bird has been reported on twelve occasions.

In *1940* one near Skibbereen, Co. Cork, May 30th to August 9th.

1957. Five at Aghadown near Skibbereen, May 9th to 29th. One at Dunfanaghy, Co. Donegal, June 2nd. One at Newcastle, Co. Wicklow, early July until September 13th. One at Blennerville, Co. Kerry, September 24th to November 3rd, a second bird arrived at Blennerville on October 22nd and stayed until November 4th.

1958. One near Clonakilty, Co. Cork, in the first week of May could possibly have been the same bird as one reported near Skibbereen from May 8th to 23rd and near Courtmacsherry 'at the end of May'.

1960. One Cape Clear Island, Co. Cork, September 26th.

1961. One at Courtmacsherry, Co. Cork, March 25th.

1962. One near Blennerville, Co. Kerry, May 29th to June 6th. One in Dunmanus Bay, Co. Cork, July 10th to August 2nd. It is conceivable that these two last reports could have been of the same bird. One at Tacumshin Lake, Co. Wexford, July 6th to September 8th.

1965. One on the North Bull, Co. Dublin on May 15th.

In each case the birds were adjacent to the coast.

Squacco Heron: *Ardeola ralloides*

Vagrant.

The eleven occurrences have taken place chiefly on the south coast in summer and autumn.

There are only three records for the present century, the last of them about 1919.

Distribution has been as follows: Kerry (2) (June 1875, September 1895); Cork (5) (May 1849; 'summer' 1850; October 1860; July 1877; May 1913); Waterford (2) (September 1895; one 'about' 1919); Derry (1) (November 1881); Mayo (1) (June 1912).

Night Heron: *Nycticorax nycticorax*

Vagrant.

There have been between thirty and forty occurrences well spaced over the years.

Occurrences have been widespread but only two have been recorded in Connacht. The majority have been in Co. Cork (9), then Dublin (5), Kerry (3 or 4), Down (3), Wexford (2), Meath (2) and in the following one each: Limerick, Leix, Offaly, Louth, Monaghan, Galway, Mayo, Armagh, Donegal.

Eleven maritime counties are represented but only six inland ones.

Where the months are known, occurrences have been in

January (1), March (3), April (2), May (7), June (2), August (2), September (2), October (2), November (7), December (1).

Just half of the birds reported have been adult.

Little Bittern: *Ixobrychus minutus*

Vagrant.

There are over forty records of the Little Bittern, ranging from January to November. Where the months are known, reports have been in May (8), April (4), November (3), March and June (1 each), February and October (1 each).

From 1830 to 1900 about thirty were recorded, since 1900 only twelve.

Occurrences have taken place chiefly in the east and south and mostly in maritime counties. Co. Cork has had almost twice as many records as Wexford, the county with the second highest number. There is only one record for Connacht.

An influx of Little Bitterns into the south of Britain in 1964 was reflected in Co. Wexford. One first seen at Rosslare on May 9th was found dead there on the 11th. Another was caught when in an exhausted state at Kilmore Quay on May 12th. Both were females.

Bittern: *Botaurus stellaris*

Formerly bred. Probably regular winter visitor.

The Bittern was breeding in Munster, Connacht and Ulster up to about 1840, since when no case of it doing so is known. 'Booming' has been heard, but without proof of breeding, in Offaly a few years before 1940, in Clare in May 1945 and in Wicklow in spring 1962.

Few winters pass without reports of one or more. Although occurrences are widespread, the majority have come from Cork and Waterford. Most are reported in December and January; the months August to March also provide records, there are one or two for May and one for July. In the last month two birds together were seen in Co. Down in 1953.

A young bird ringed in Suffolk in May was recovered the following November in Co. Longford.

American Bittern: *Botaurus lentiginosus*
Vagrant.

Nineteen have been recorded: in Munster eight, Leinster five, Ulster five, Connacht one, in December 1964. Occurrences have been chiefly in October and November; there are records for December, January and February.

White Stork: *Ciconia ciconia*
Four records.

One was shot near Fermoy, Co. Cork, in May 1846; two others were stated to have been with it. One was obtained near the Wexford coast in the autumn of 1846. One was killed on the River Lee, Co. Cork, on August 7th 1866. One was seen near Tuam, Co. Galway, on December 19th 1909.

Two further instances mentioned in *Birds of Ireland* (1900), p. 170, are excluded as there is too much doubt about them.

Spoonbill: *Platalea leucorodia*
Irregular visitor.

Between 1829 and 1900 there were 33 records concerning a total of 54 birds; since 1900 there have been 49 occurrences with a total of 113 birds.

Occurrences have been well spread over the years and have been in maritime counties, mostly in those of the south, with Co. Cork heading the list.

The majority of Spoonbills have been seen in the latter half of the year, but there are records for every month.

The Spoonbill is most often seen singly. In eight instances two or more were together, in one case seven, in another five.

Very often birds have made prolonged stays, remaining in a locality for several months. In one instance a Spoonbill was present for almost a year and on more than one occasion birds have wintered.

Glossy Ibis: *Plegadis falcinellus*
Irregular visitor, chiefly in autumn.

About 56 occurrences have been recorded, mostly in the

maritime counties of the south, Cork, Wexford and Waterford having had the majority. There are instances of the bird in Dublin, Offaly, Westmeath, Longford, Galway, Down, Antrim, Derry and Donegal.

Occurrences have taken place in January (2), February (2), June (1), August (1), September (6), October (8), November (5) and October or November (4), November or December (1). These numbers exclude those of the winter 1945–46 when a remarkable number was seen or shot between November 18th and mid-February and in widespread localities covering six counties. The autumn of 1906 was also notable for occurrences which took place in seven counties.

On several occasions birds have remained to winter.

The exceptional number of twenty stayed for about ten days in Co. Wexford in October 1934; smaller parties have sometimes been seen.

No occurrence was recorded between 1882 and 1900. The only report since 1946 is of one shot in Co. Westmeath on October 9th 1959.

Flamingo: *Phoenicopterus ruber*

Two, possibly four, have been recorded.

A Flamingo was seen on the River Foyle near Derry City on April 3rd and 27th 1938. One that was near Timoleague, Co. Cork, from May 1st to June 4th 1938 and one near Askeaton, Co. Limerick, in early November 1938 could either or both have been the one seen on the Foyle. One was shot near Dundalk, Co. Louth, in the first week of September 1947.

The possibility that these occurrences were of 'escapes' cannot be excluded.

Mallard: *Anas platyrhynchos*

Resident. Winter visitor.

The Mallard breeds in every county and on some remote marine islands.

The resident population is mainly sedentary, performing only local movements. After the breeding season and before immigrants arrive, concentrations form. In these several hundreds are seen, the maximum in recent years being about 3,500; in one single flock there were 1,700 birds.

In autumn and winter there is extensive immigration from Scotland, the Continent and Iceland.

There are many waters in all the provinces where assemblies of 500 or more occur in winter. Small numbers also frequent tidal waters.

Black Duck: *Anas rubripes*

Two records.

A female was shot at Mullinavat, Co. Kilkenny, about February 13th 1954. One was identified on the North Slob, Co. Wexford, on February 18th 1961; it was still present on the 21st.

Teal: *Anas crecca*

Resident. Winter visitor.

The Teal breeds throughout the country, in some cases at high mountain lakes. Home bred birds are largely sedentary or subject to local movements only.

Immigration commences at the end of October, though an Iceland ringed juvenile was recovered on August 20th following. Large numbers from Scotland, northern England, the Continent, even as far afield as Russia and Finland, and from Iceland winter in Ireland.

Probably the greatest concentration is to be found in winter on the channel adjacent to the North Bull, Co. Dublin. Here many hundreds congregate. Teal frequent many inland waters; in recent years assemblies of about 200 and sometimes 350 have been reported. On Lough Beg, Co. Derry, about 1,500 were counted on February 5th 1959, following hard weather; the normal winter figure there is under 1,000.

In Connacht, though much in evidence in autumn, numbers diminish in winter, but increase again in March.

The Green-winged Teal (*Anas c. carolinensis*) has been recorded ten times.

Two males near Ballycolla, Leix, November 30th 1953. A male at Akeagh Lough, Co. Kerry, February 16th 1955, was accompanied by a female possibly of this race. Single males at Blennerville,

Co. Kerry, October 27th 1956; at Downpatrick marshes, Down, on February 16th 1958; at Akeagh Lough, November 23rd 1958; at Killag, Co. Wexford, April 18th 1959; near Kilcoole, Co. Wicklow, April 14th 1962; near Blennerville, January 19th 1964 and March 21st 1965; at Akeagh Lough, October 17th 1965.

Garganey: *Anas querquedula*

Has bred. Vagrant.

In 1956 a pair bred successfully on Lough Neagh. In 1959 a pair bred in Co. Kerry. 1959 was a year remarkable for the number of occurrences in which a total of twenty-two birds were reported, on one occasion five males together.

The Garganey has been recorded about sixty-two times, about ninety-one birds being concerned.

Occurrences have become increasingly frequent and since 1953 have been annual, except for 1955.

Cork, Kerry and Wexford have supplied the majority of records, but birds have been reported in Clare, Limerick, Tipperary, Wicklow, Dublin, Carlow, Leix, Offaly, Westmeath, Roscommon, Mayo, Fermanagh, Down, Antrim and Derry.

Dated occurrences have preponderated in March (10), and April (11) but have taken place in January (6), February (5), May (8), June (2), August (6), September (3), November (5), December (3).

Garganey ringed on the Continent have been recovered in winter in widely separated localities.

Blue-winged Teal: *Anas discors*

Eight records.

An immature female, September 1910, Ballycotton, Co. Cork; a female, November 1932, on the River Shannon near Limerick; an adult male, January 1949, near Dundalk, Co. Louth; an adult female, December 1950, at Garryvoe, Co. Cork; a female, November 1955, near Leap, Co. Cork; a female, January 1956, on Downpatrick marshes, Co. Down; one, September 1957, at Lough Beg, Co. Derry; an immature male or female, October 1962, near Portumna, Co. Galway; an immature male or female, October 1962, in Co. Kilkenny near New Ross. All were shot.

Gadwall: *Anas strepera*

Scarce resident. Passage migrant. Winter visitor.

Since 1933 a very few have bred in Cos. Armagh, Fermanagh, Roscommon, Donegal; breeding has been suspected in Co. Mayo.

Before 1900 the Gadwall was a scarce and irregular visitor. Since then it has been increasingly recorded, and by about 1953 had become more numerous and widespread, particularly at times of passage. Gadwall have occurred in every county, but the largest numbers are found in those of the west. Until recently it was seldom seen in the south-east, but now occurs regularly.

At certain favoured waters Gadwall appear in considerable numbers during spring passage. Many are then in pairs. The greatest concentrations occur at Akeagh Lough and Lough Gill in Co. Kerry in February and April. Over 280 have been seen at Akeagh Lough and numbers of up to 250 are almost annual at migration periods.

In Co. Galway a favoured water has fluctuating numbers on a much smaller scale than those in Kerry; the maximum numbers are seen in March and April when fifty have been counted, once 150 to 200 in February.

On the Little Brosna and River Shannon near Banagher in Offaly large numbers have occurred in March.

From mid-September autumn arrivals occur and again the Co. Kerry numbers are greatest. They rise through October to a maximum in November when 122 have been counted on Lough Gill. Gadwall are regular in winter at Akeagh Lough; an exceptional maximum in January was 162.

Elsewhere in Ireland it is found as a scattered visitor in small numbers only.

Other than for breeding birds there are records in June (1), July (3), August (1).

Ringing results indicate that immigrants come from Iceland.

Wigeon: *Anas penelope*

Has bred. Winter visitor.

Breeding in Ireland was long suspected before it was proved in 1933 in Co. Armagh. A pair bred on Rathlin Island in 1953. There is no recent evidence of breeding.

Winter visitors arrive in September, rarely at the end of August, and become abundant in October. In 1965 arrivals were reported at two localities in Co. Derry, on August 11th and 18th respectively.

In March and April most depart, but some remain into May.

Concentrations of 500 birds are frequent. In December and January maximum numbers recorded together have been 2,000 or over.

The majority of immigrants come from Iceland, but a proportion are from Scotland and the Continent, including Russia.

Baldpate: *Anas americana*

Three records.

A male and female were seen near the North Bull, Co. Dublin, February 23rd and 27th 1954. A male was shot on Strangford Lough, Co. Down, on January 31st 1963: the specimen is in the Ulster Museum, Belfast. A male was shot at Trawbreaga Bay, Co. Donegal, on September 26th 1964.

Baldpates are now widely kept in wildfowl collections in Britain and the possibility of birds reported in recent years being 'escapes' must be considered.

Pintail: *Anas acuta*

Rare resident. Winter visitor. Probable passage migrant.

Though long suspected of breeding in Ireland, the first proof was in 1917 when a nest was found in Co. Roscommon. Since then a few pairs have bred, though there is no proof of their doing so recently, in Armagh, Antrim and Down. In 1932 it bred in Leix, in 1959 in Derry.

The Pintail has increased during the present century and especially inland since 1940. In favoured resorts it is abundant in winter. In recent years 500 have been counted on some occasions at Rahasane, Co. Galway; 300 annually, but sometimes more, at the North Bull, Co. Dublin, and 200 near Banagher in Offaly. In Castlemaine Harbour, Co. Kerry, about 800 were recorded in October 1954; there were 700 at Lough Beg, Co. Derry, in February 1959, 940 on March 14th 1965, figures above average; normally the maximum there is about 450. Many places hold 100 birds.

In Tipperary and Cavan and a number of other inland counties Pintail are scarce. For Co. Carlow there is no record.

The earliest immigrants arrive at the end of September; by mid-October Pintail are numerous. After an abundance in October and November numbers diminish but increase again in March. Most depart about mid-April; some linger into May. Birds on spring migration, even when in flocks, are quite evidently already paired.

Immigrants come chiefly from Iceland, but also from Scotland and the Continent.

The turloughs of Connacht are much favoured, Pintail seldom being found on the large deep lakes.

Shoveler: *Spatula clypeata*

Resident. Passage migrant. Winter visitor.

In 1850 the Shoveler was an uncommon winter visitor. Since 1900 winter numbers have greatly increased.

At the end of last century the Shoveler was breeding in eighteen counties, though sparsely in some. Five more counties had been added by 1950 and the only counties where breeding now falls short of proof are Carlow, Kilkenny, Kildare, Meath and Leitrim. It is doubtful whether any breed in Wexford or Louth where formerly some evidently did so.

A large immigration occurs in October and continues in winter. Numbers reach a maximum in March and April. In winter loose flocks containing 300 birds are frequent, sometimes of 500; about 900 were seen on the River Slaney estuary, Co. Wexford, in February 1962. The largest counts at Lough Beg, Co. Derry, are of between 400 and 550 birds, the peak numbers being in March

Immigrants come from the Continent, even from Russia; some come from Iceland.

Red-crested Pochard: *Netta rufina*

Ten records.

A male near Tralee, Co. Kerry, January 18th 1881; a male at Reendonogan Lake, near Bantry, Co. Cork, December 29th 1927; two males on the South Slob, Co. Wexford, January 31st 1949; a male and a female or immature bird, Galway Bay, November 2nd 1952; a female or immature bird, Cappagh, Co. Waterford, December 27th 1952; a female on the River Blackwater, Co. Meath, January 26th 1958; a male at Tacumshin Lake, Co.

Wexford, October 8th 1961; a male in Dingle Harbour, Co. Kerry, January 12th 1963; a male, Lough Neagh, on the Armagh shore, March 14th 1965; one Shane's Castle, Co. Antrim, November 11th 1965. Except for the two seen in Galway Bay, the Lough Neagh bird and the one in Dingle Harbour, all were shot.

Scaup: *Aythya marila*

Occasional non-breeding summer visitor. Winter visitor.

Pairs linger in Connacht into April and May, sometimes to June, July and August.

A flock of about fifty were on the sea off the coast of Co. Meath on July 22nd 1963.

As a winter visitor this duck is locally abundant, frequenting bays and estuaries, rarely fresh water unless adjacent to the coast.

Scaup occur increasingly on Lough Neagh, especially in March and November when well over 1,000 have been counted. On several occasions they have been recorded far up the River Shannon. A flock of about twenty were on Lough Ennell, Co. Westmeath, on December 12th 1953.

Early arrivals have been noted on the South Slob, Co. Wexford, on August 22nd, numbers increasing in early September, in which month immigration is at its height. Some recent counts in Wexford Harbour and on the South Slob, where previous to 1950 200 were rarely seen, indicate a great increase—1,500 to 2,000 February 2nd 1960; at least 2,000 February 15th 1961; 2,000 to 3,000 January 18th 1962. Before the destruction by severe weather in January 1963 of the feeding grounds off Laytown, Co. Meath, 500 to 1,000 were sometimes seen there, though normally 200 to 300. Now few are found. Recently up to 1,000 have been seen in winter in Dundrum Bay, Co. Down, and Carlingford Lough is increasingly resorted to, about 1,000 were there in January 1965.

The Scaup is scarce on the west coast south of Co. Mayo and on the south coast.

Belfast Lough, due to reclamation of the feeding grounds, no longer holds great numbers; they are steadily decreasing and in 1964 numbered about 400. Numbers in Lough Foyle have declined to negligible proportions.

Departure is in March and April.

Most of the winter visitors come from Iceland.

Tufted Duck: *Aythya fuligula*
Resident. Winter visitor.

First bred in 1877. Since 1900 it has increased markedly both as a breeding bird and as a winter visitor. Tufted Duck now breed, often in considerable numbers, in all counties except Waterford, Wexford, Carlow, Meath, Louth and Kildare (where formerly it bred temporarily in one locality). In Kerry it is very scarce and local.

On Lough Neagh the increase has been remarkable. In 1922 a few pairs bred for the first time; within twenty years over a hundred nests could be found on a single island.

A considerable immigration commences at the end of September and continues in early October, the latter being the peak period of arrival. Numbers are often augmented, even in mild winters, at the end of November.

On many waters flocks of 50 to 100 and considerably greater totals are noted. About 21,800 were reported on Lough Neagh on January 17th 1960, nearly 18,000 on January 17th and over 25,000 on October 17th 1965. On Lough Beg, Co. Derry, the most notable counts are five of between 2,400 and 3,800 birds in January and February, October and March.

In March the large flocks depart.

In addition to winter visitors from Iceland, many come from the Continent.

In the winter flocks there is normally a two to one excess of males over females.

Ring-necked Duck: *Aythya collaris*
One recorded.

An adult male frequented Lurgan Park Lake, Co. Armagh, from March 20th 1960 until at least mid-March 1961. At times it would absent itself and was clearly the bird reported on Lough Neagh on December 4th 1960. It is believed that this same bird was the one seen at Lurgan Park in October and November 1963, in November and December 1964 and November 1965.

Pochard: *Aythya ferina*
Scarce resident. Winter visitor.

The Pochard had long been suspected of breeding very locally.

It did so in Co. Monaghan in 1907. From 1930 onwards a few pairs nested in Co. Roscommon. In Leix it bred in 1931. Two pairs bred at Levally Lough, Co. Galway, from 1950 until the lake was drained in 1956. Two pairs bred in Co. Tipperary in 1952, a pair at Lough Beg, Co. Derry, in 1958 and a pair in Co. Galway in 1962. Breeding in recent years has been suspected on Rathlin Island, Lough Neagh, Lough Erne and in Co. Donegal.

The first winter flocks appear regularly about mid-October, but earlier arrivals occur towards the end of September; in 1964 over 500 were on Lough Gara, Co. Roscommon, on August 30th. On Lough Beg, Co. Derry, the Pochard flock in one year began to build up in July and by August 17th had reached a strength of seventy. Another early record is of a flock in Co. Wexford on August 22nd.

The Pochard is widespread inland, but not numerous on tidal waters. It is found in considerable numbers on turloughs in Connacht and on large lakes. Many hundreds are found on the Mullet, Co. Mayo. There are some high figures for Lough Beg, Co. Derry: there is a build-up there during winter from about 800 to over 2,400 birds. At least 1,000 were seen at Rahasane, Co. Galway, in December 1963. The maximum counts are of at least 4,700 on Lough Beg on November 29th 1964, nearly 7,000 in January, 7,500 in November 1965 and over 14,000 in February 1965 on Lough Neagh.

Departure is at the end of March, though non-breeding birds are often seen in summer.

The only evidence of the origin of immigrants is of three from the Continent.

Winter flocks usually contain a large male preponderance; this can be as much as 89%.

Ferruginous Duck: *Aythya nyroca*

Vagrant.

There are twelve records concerning sixteen birds.

Occurrences have been widespread—Wexford (2), Dublin (1), Westmeath (1), Meath (1), Down (2), Antrim (1), River Shannon (2), East coast (1), county unknown (1).

Where dates are known, occurrences have been in January (3), February (1), March (2), November (3), December (1).

Goldeneye: *Bucephala clangula*
Winter visitor. Occasionally in summer.

The Goldeneye is found in estuaries, bays and on fresh water in all parts of Ireland, but is scarce generally on the Connacht coast. It is considered the most numerous of the ducks on Lower Lough Erne. The Goldeneye is thought to have increased during this century.

Goldeneyes are usually found in parties of up to ten or twelve birds, but flocks of 100 to 500 have been reported. On Lough Beg, Co. Derry, the normal winter population varies between 80 and 200 birds; about 450 were seen in February 1956. On the coast of Co. Meath 500 together have been noted. About 1,900 were reported in February 1959 on Lough Neagh; about 2,800 in January 1960.

Though a flock of twelve has been seen on August 25th and two birds elsewhere on September 12th, the first arrivals are only very rarely reported in early October, more usually in late October. Numbers increase noticeably at the end of November and in early December.

Departure is almost complete by April following local increases, no doubt of moving birds, that take place in March.

Birds, sometimes in pairs, are seen occasionally on inland waters in April, even in May. There are several June records, one or two for July.

Long-tailed Duck: *Clangula hyemalis*
Winter visitor.

Though a regular winter visitor, this duck occurs in very variable numbers and is somewhat irregular in the localities it visits. It occurs on all coasts, the tidal waters of the south coast being the least frequented, those of the north-west most regularly and by the greatest numbers. It is increasingly reported in Co. Wexford.

Usually this duck is seen singly or in numbers less than six, but in the past a flock of 50 was recorded in Killala Bay, Co. Mayo. More recently flocks of 40 to 50, 26 and 20 have been seen on the west coast. Numbers of up to 30 off Portnoo, Co. Donegal, are considered regular there. A flock of 33 spent at least ten days in Inishfree Bay, Co. Donegal, in April 1962.

It occurs at times far inland, usually singly. A flock of about twenty spent most of the winter 1899–1900 on Lough Corrib.

This duck arrives in October and is seen up to April, occasionally mid-May. In June 1933 an adult pair stayed for a week in a bay in Co. Cork.

Velvet Scoter: *Melanitta fusca*

Scarce winter visitor. Occasional at other seasons.

At times over a series of years the Velvet Scoter has not been recorded. Nowadays in most winters one to three or more are reported.

Before 1900 Drogheda Bay produced the majority of records and no doubt up to 1963 there was a small but regular wintering population there, the birds being mixed with the large flocks of Common Scoter. A sample count in November 1963 and other observations indicated that up to twenty wintered off the coast between Balbriggan, Co. Dublin, and the River Boyne mouth.

The severe weather and easterly gales in January 1963 followed by constant strong easterly winds in the winter 1963–64 decimated the shellfish beds and the scoters have deserted the area.

In Dundrum Bay, Co. Down, five were found amongst the Common Scoters in February 1964. Single birds are not infrequently seen close to the shore in this bay.

Although the coasts of Dublin, Louth and Down have supplied most records, all coasts are visited. The Velvet Scoter has thrice been obtained inland.

Occurrences have been reported between early September and June: September (3), October (6), November (8), December (5), January (11), February (7), March (6), April (1), May (2), June (3).

In September and October single birds have been seen flying westward off Cape Clear, Co. Cork, and two off Hook Head, Co. Wexford, in September.

Surf Scoter: *Melanitta perspicillata*

Six records concerning seven birds.

An adult male in Ballyholme Bay, Co. Down, September 9th 1846. An adult male at Clontarf, Co. Dublin, in October 1880. An immature bird in Crookhaven Bay, Co. Cork, November 5th 1888.

Photo: David Cabot

PART OF THE NORTH SLOB, CO. WEXFORD

RAHASANE TURLOUGH,

Photo: David Cabot

CO. GALWAY

Plate 3

Photo: Ian Finlay

TIDAL FLATS OFF KILBARRACK, CHANNEL AND NORTH POINT OF NORTH BULL, CO. DUBLIN. HAUNTS OF BRENT GEESE, DUCKS AND WADERS.

An immature female at Achill Island, Co. Mayo, October 25th 1890. A male and female in Killala Bay, Co. Mayo, December 19th 1896. All these were shot. An immature bird was off the North Bull Island, Co. Dublin, from November 3rd to December 20th 1958.

Common Scoter: *Melanitta nigra*

Summer visitor. Breeds in two localities. Perhaps passage migrant. Winter visitor.

Nests were found in 1905 in Co. Fermanagh where it had probably bred in 1904. Breeding continues with some signs of an increase to over fifty pairs.

Breeding in Co. Mayo was suspected in 1940 and was proved in 1948. Numbers had slowly increased to between twenty and thirty breeding pairs, but since 1963 a drop in numbers is suspected.

Common Scoters are rarely found inland except where breeding; on Lough Neagh, however, the bird is not infrequent.

Occurrences off the coasts are widespread in June, July and August; most are of single birds in June, of small parties seldom exceeding fifty birds in July and August. Notable exceptions are Ballyheigue, Brandon and Dingle Bays, Co. Kerry, in which there is a considerable summer population. Numbers vary from year to year; in Dingle Bay the average is about 200, but 2,500 and 5,000 have been reported in different years in July and August. Numbers in the other two bays are smaller.

Up to 1963 on the Co. Meath coast a total of seventy to eighty was regular from June to August; off Co. Louth a hundred or more were found and off Balbriggan, Co. Dublin, about fifty. These places were favourite winter haunts. It is surprising therefore that the similarly favoured Wexford coast had no summer population.

At Cape Clear, Co. Cork, a westward small-scale passage is noticed in July and early August.

A noticeable increase in numbers commences in September, reaching its peak in November. Dingle Bay holds about 1,500 in winter; Brandon Bay about 200; Ballyheigue Bay about 100. It seems that very few indeed were present in these haunts in the winter 1964–65.

The average wintering strength in Dundrum Bay, Co. Down,

was 1,200, but 2,000 have been reported, in early 1965 less than 100–200 were present, in the early winter of 1965 under 50.

From Clogher Head, Co. Lough, southward to Skerries, Co. Dublin, and especially off Laytown, Co. Meath, a winter population of between 2,000 and 3,000 was regular until 1964. Off Arklow, Co. Wicklow, Courtown, Co. Wexford, and in Wexford Bay the winter population was about 1,200.

Consequent upon the decimation of their food supply due to the severe cold and high easterly winds in January 1963 and the final destruction due to easterly gales in winter 1963–64, the Common Scoters have virtually deserted the coastline from Dundrum Bay to Wexford Bay. A flock of 200 to 300 frequented a bay a few miles north of Arklow for part of the winter 1964–65 but were absent in early winter 1965. Elsewhere only a few scattered parties of five or six birds, very rarely of over twenty, are found. Thus when food supplies become scarce, as can happen following or even during exceptionally severe winters, there is a tremendous drop in the numbers of Common Scoters frequenting our coasts.

Common Scoters are locally plentiful off the west coast of Co. Donegal: in Loughros More Bay over 200 have been reported. Large rafts are no longer seen in Sligo Bay. The bird is very scarce or absent on the west coast southward from the Mullet, Co. Mayo, until the Kerry coast is reached.

In recent years a marked decrease in numbers has taken place in the following haunts, due, it is said, to the loss of feeding grounds: in Belfast Lough where formerly there were great numbers the strength is about twenty birds in the south half of the lough. Lough Foyle and Lough Swilly have been deserted, the former since about 1935. In Killala Bay previous to 1962 the estimated number was between 1,000 and 2,000 but was considered to be decreasing and in 1964 the maximum number was put at 1,000, perhaps as few as between 500 and 700, in 1965 even fewer.

Eider: *Somateria mollissima*
Resident.

Since breeding first took place in 1912 at Inishtrahull off the Donegal coast, the range has extended to islands and the mainland of that county. Numbers have greatly increased. In 1962 the number breeding on Inishtrahull exceeded a hundred. Inishmurray,

Co. Sligo, was colonised about 1961; about twenty pairs were breeding there in 1964. Eiders breed on islands off Co. Antrim and Co. Down and also on the mainland.

After the breeding season flocks are seen on the Donegal coast, maximum numbers recently recorded being a flock of 160 off Rosbeg in July; 600 in scattered parties off Malin Head in August; 200 off Inishtrahull in September.

The Eider occurs irregularly off most of the maritime counties in the southern half of the country: dates are between August 10th off Co. Galway and April 14th off Co. Wexford. This last bird remained until at least October 13th. Normally birds are seen singly but there were at least five in Dingle Bay, Co. Kerry, in October 1958.

The Eider has twice been obtained on Lough Neagh.

King Eider: *Somateria spectabilis*

Five records.

The five occurrences have taken place between November 10th and March 11th and at long intervals.

A female in Belfast Lough, March 11th 1850; a female on Rathlin Island, Co. Antrim, on November 20th 1861; an immature male off Achill Island, Co. Mayo, December 12th 1892; an adult male off Co. Down, November 10th 1897. All these were shot. One was seen off Baltimore, Co. Cork, on many occasions between January 29th and February 24th 1959.

Too much doubt exists about one recorded in Co. Dublin in 1837 to allow of its acceptance.

Red-breasted Merganser: *Mergus serrator*

Resident. Winter visitor.

There has been an extension in breeding range and an increase in numbers since the beginning of this century. It now breeds in all counties except Limerick, Waterford, Wicklow, Kildare, Carlow, Offaly, Louth and Monaghan. It still breeds sparsely in the south-east. In addition to the larger lakes, marine loughs and islands are resorted to for nesting.

Immature and non-breeding birds frequent coastal bays and estuaries throughout summer: a hundred or more together have been recorded; 250 in Dundrum Bay, Co. Down, on June 29th.

After breeding most leave inland waters but a few remain all winter. From autumn until spring this duck is numerous on tidal waters where assemblies of less than fifty birds are general. Maximum counts include 366 in Belfast Lough in September, 250 in December.

An adult ringed in Ireland in June was recovered in northern Scotland the following March.

Goosander: *Mergus merganser*

Scarce winter visitor.

The Goosander is of annual occurrence. Numbers reported vary between two and seven. There have been records of eight together; on a lake in Co. Monaghan twenty-one were counted in January 1945, sixteen in the following December.

Occurrences fall between September 4th (1) and April 25th (4): the majority are seen in December (33), January (36), February (19). One was recorded in summer.

Few have been found west of the River Shannon; elsewhere the distribution of occurrences has been widespread.

Inland and tidal waters are frequented.

In the severe winter of 1880–81 and in January and February 1963 records were above average.

Smew: *Mergus albellus*

Scarce winter visitor.

In almost every winter one to four are reported. Smew are most often seen singly, but up to five together have been reported. A large majority of the records come from Leinster and Ulster; for Connacht only two instances are known—Mayo (1), Leitrim (1). Previous records for Mayo are unacceptable.

Most records are for December (29), January (30) and February (19). The Smew has occurred in November (6), March (5) and April (1). Adult males are rare.

Hooded Merganser: *Mergus cucullatus*

Three records involving four birds.

A male and female were shot in Cobh Harbour, Co. Cork, in December 1878. A female was shot in the Shannon estuary, off Ballylongford, Co. Kerry, in January 1881. A female or immature bird was seen at Acton Lake, Co. Armagh, on December 21st 1957.

Shelduck: *Tadorna tadorna*

Resident. Temporary emigrant. Probable winter visitor.

Leitrim is the only maritime county in which there is no evidence of breeding. Very few breed in Co. Galway.

Inland the Shelduck has bred on Lough Neagh and Lower Lough Erne; about ten pairs do so on Lough Beg, Co. Derry.

Most emigrate after the breeding season, probably proceeding to Heligoland Bight for the moult. They are scarce in July and August but return in October. Maximum numbers are found from December to April and the bird is then generally distributed in suitable localities on all coasts.

Gatherings of 200 are often seen; on February 8th 1956, 511 were counted off the North Bull, Co. Dublin; in Belfast Lough, where numbers build up to a maximum in January and February, about 860 were counted on February 6th 1965.

The occasional inland occurrences take place in autumn or winter, more rarely in spring. Seven together were seen on Lough Carra, Co. Mayo, in September.

A juvenile ringed in Norway was recovered in Co. Waterford the following January.

Ruddy Shelduck: *Casarca ferruginea*

Irregular vagrant.

There were scattered records of one to three birds in 1847, 1869, 1871. In June and July 1886 there was an immigration of parties up to six strong. In the summer of 1892 the visitation was more extensive: records were widespread and flocks of up to twenty birds were reported.

Since 1892 the few recorded in 1945 and 1946 were in winter; on three occasions three birds were together, on another only one.

A single bird in September 1955 was almost certainly an 'escape'; single birds must always be suspect.

Grey Lag Goose: *Anser anser*
Winter visitor.

In 1900 this goose was unknown in Co. Wexford and Co. Down, but soon afterwards became numerous. Since about 1950 there has been a great decrease in the wintering numbers.

The Wexford slobs were its chief stronghold and up to 1949 6,000 or more were found there. Since 1954 flocks of about ten birds occasionally visit the North Slob. In December 1963 one of about 300 birds stayed for a few days. Most often there are no Grey Lag Geese there. The number (50 to 80) visiting marshes near Newcastle, Co. Wicklow, is less than half that of former years. Relatively few now come to Downpatrick marshes, Co. Down. The Inish, Co. Wexford, and haunts in Co. Dublin and Co. Louth have been deserted. A flock of about 200 winters at Poulaphouca reservoir, Co. Wicklow. On Lough Foyle, Co. Derry, there is a haunt of 300 to 400. No other worthwhile populations are known, though at single haunts in Waterford, Tipperary, Cork and Limerick and at the north-east corner of Lough Neagh less than twenty-five are found.

On November 13th 1960 the total number in Ireland did not exceed 500. Peak numbers are, however, attained in December and January.

Small flocks are irregularly reported from scattered localities, least often west of the River Shannon and most often at times of migration.

The Grey Lag arrives in mid-October; it has once been reported on August 28th. Most have departed by mid-April; stragglers remain into May. There are two records for mid-June.

Most of our Grey Lags probably come from Iceland; birds move to Ireland from Scottish winter haunts.

This is probably the species of goose stated to have bred in Ireland in the eighteenth century.

Because of the marked change in distribution and numbers that has taken place in recent years, the following papers are mentioned for detailed study.

'The distribution and status of Wild Geese in Ireland,' *Bird Study*, 5: 22 and map p. 23. 'Grey Lag Geese in Britain in winter,' *The Wildfowl Trust*, 10th Annual Report 1957–58, pp. 43–58.

White-fronted Goose: *Anser albifrons*

Anser a. albifrons: Less than ten records.

Four were shot at Ballough, Co. Dublin, on January 5th 1947, from a flock of eleven White-fronted Geese which were probably of the nominate form. A few days later another was shot. Five more were shot in the same place in February out of a flock of fifty birds. On February 26th ten or twelve with the characteristics of this form were seen. Some of the same birds may have been concerned in some of the above records. Weather was very severe at the time.

An adult shot on February 20th 1948 near Ballycroy, Co. Mayo, was probably of the typical form. Three were identified beside Lough Neagh, Co. Antrim, on December 31st 1956. Two were seen on the South Slob, Co. Wexford, on February 21st 1961.

Anser a. flavirostris: Winter visitor.

The Greenland White-fronted Goose is an abundant winter visitor. The total wintering is probably between 9,000 and 10,000. The chief haunt is the North Slob, Co. Wexford; normally 3,000 to 5,000 winter there, showing a recent slight decrease due to extensive tillage. In February 1962 about 7,000 were estimated on the slobs; in November 1964 there were 4,680 on the North, 2,380 on the South Slob. Due to the extensive ploughing that now takes place in January on the South Slob, numbers there decrease to about 200 or 300 from that month.

Reclamation has driven them from the Inish near Kilmore Quay, Co. Wexford.

About 1,000 are found along the River Shannon between Clonmacnoise and Portumna. This goose frequents the great bogs of the midlands, Connacht and Donegal in scattered small flocks; estimation of the total is difficult.

Callow land is much favoured, also grassy islands in lakes. In such places numbers between 100 and 300 are found; haunts holding about fifty birds are widespread.

Seemingly suitable habitats in Wicklow, Kerry, Dublin, Cavan and Monaghan are not much used. In Cork and Waterford this goose is virtually unknown.

Following extensive reclamation on Lambay, Co. Dublin, a flock of at least 100 has wintered since 1959.

There is a record of seven seen in Kerry on August 3rd, of four in Wexford on August 16th. Arrivals normally take place from the third week of September, more usually from early October. Full strength is reached in early November. Departure is in April; stragglers remain into May, in which month there are records for 1st, 23rd and 25th.

The race has its origin in Greenland whence our winter visitors come.

Bean Goose: *Anser arvensis*

Occasional in winter.

It is problematical whether the Bean Goose was ever so widespread and common as formerly stated.

There have been few occurrences in this century. Between 1917 and 1927 only nine were reported, thereafter none until 1946. The following are the only acceptable recent records. In the Bog of Erris, Co. Mayo, three were shot from a flock of four on December 31st 1946. Two were shot at Tynan Abbey, Co. Armagh, on January 4th 1956. One was seen in Strangford Lough, Co. Down, on February 18th 1956. A goose almost certainly of this species was shot on the Mullet, Co. Mayo, in December 1956. One was seen near Kilcoole, Co. Wicklow, on March 17th 1960.

Pink-footed Goose: *Anser brachyrhynchus*

Winter visitor.

This goose is reported every winter. Most occurrences are of single birds or parties of less than six.

A flock of fifty was recorded in Co. Wicklow on January 30th 1945; one of twenty-seven in Co. Donegal on September 26th 1964; one of about twelve in Co. Wexford in January 1944.

One or two birds are reported annually on the Wexford slobs, otherwise there is no regular haunt of this goose in Ireland. Occurrences have been well scattered and embrace the counties Limerick, Kerry, Wicklow, Dublin, Offaly, Meath, Westmeath, Louth, Roscommon, Galway, Mayo, Sligo, Donegal, Down and Antrim.

Earliest date September 24th, latest (of two birds in Kerry), May 2nd.

Before 1900 there were only two records. The fact that this goose is now found regularly may well be due to more intensive watching and recording.

Recoveries of ringed birds indicate that our visitors come not only from Iceland, but that some move across from Britain during the winter.

Snow Goose: *Anser caerulescens*

Vagrant.

There have been at least twenty-two records of the Snow Goose, the race to which they belonged being indeterminate.

Occurrences have been from October to May.

Most have been reported in Co. Mayo, then in Co. Wexford. There are records for Kerry, Dublin, Longford, Westmeath, Galway, Donegal, Down.

Dates range from October 26th to February 29th; one on May 23rd.

Nowadays most often seen singly, but eight, twelve, fourteen together have been reported in this century.

The possibility that some have been 'escapes' cannot be overlooked.

Lesser Snow Goose: *Anser c. caerulescens*

Four records.

Two were shot at Tacumshin Lake, Co. Wexford, in November 1871. A male was shot at Grey Abbey, Co. Down, in January 1941. An adult wintered on the North Slob, Co. Wexford, 1953–54 and one 1958–59.

Some of the records under Snow Goose may refer to this, the nominate form.

Lesser Snow Goose: Blue phase.
Less than ten records.

In January and April 1946 three Blue Geese, two of them immature, were seen on the North Slob, Co. Wexford. In the years following, single adults, on several occasions with an accompanying immature, wintered.

Those seen in winters 1948–49 and 1949–50 were probably the same birds, as were possibly those of 1951–52 and 1952–53. The adult and immature birds in the winters 1953–54 to 1956–57 were probably the same ones each year. In the winter 1957–58 the single adult was shot and no Blue Goose was present in winter 1958–59. An adult in winter 1959–60 was a fresh arrival and, by reason of a leg injury, was recognisable as the bird present in 1960–61. Since then no Blue Goose has been seen.

It is almost certain therefore that less than ten different birds are known to have come to Ireland. It is highly probable, from evidence collected, that the birds have been genuine vagrants. A Blue Goose was seen to arrive on the slob with the first small flocks of Greenland White-fronted Geese.

In at least one case interbreeding between a Blue Goose and a Greenland White-fronted Goose had taken place.

Greater Snow Goose: *Anser. c. atlanticus*
Two records.

Two were shot out of a flock of seven Snow Geese at Termoncarragh, on the Mullet, Co. Mayo, in October 1877. One of these was definitely referable to this form. One was shot near Belmullet, Co. Mayo, in October 1886.

It is probable that some of the records given under Snow Goose refer to this race.

Brent Goose: *Branta bernicla*
Dark-breasted Brent Goose: *Branta b. bernicla*
Vagrant.

Only thirteen occurrences of this the nominate form are known. Of these four were obtained, two of them on the Dublin coast in

December 1903 and December 1909, two in Co. Down in November 1916 and in winter 1938–39.

Sight records have been of single birds in five cases, two birds together in three instances; once of a flock of five off Sutton, Co. Dublin, where the birds remained from January 16th to February 6th 1954. The earliest was recorded on October 7th in Co. Kerry.

Months of occurrence have been October (2), November (2), December (4), January (2), February (1), March (1) and the years 1903, 1909, 1916, 1938–39, 1954 (2), 1956, 1957 (2), 1958, 1960, 1963, 1965; the counties Kerry (3), Down (3), Dublin (7).

Pale-breasted Brent Goose: *Branta b. hrota*
Winter visitor.

Following a marked decrease in numbers earlier in this century, this goose has staged a recovery. While numbers fall short of those found in the nineteenth century, there has been a substantial increase during the past ten, more especially in the last two or three years.

The total present in the peak period in winter is about 12,000; in 1950 it was about 6,000.

The following are the main haunts and approximate population strength in November and December: Lough Foyle, 850; Larne Lough, 100; Strangford Lough, 3,650; North Bull, 150; Wexford Harbour, 600; Bannow Bay, 50; Tramore Strand, 20; Dungarvan Harbour, 30; Tralee Bay, 3,500; Castlemaine Harbour, 3,000; Galway Bay, 70; Sligo Bay, 500; Trawbreaga Bay, 50.

In early January there is a change in numbers in some haunts. The Strangford Lough population suddenly drops to about 1,000 birds; at the same time on the Dublin coast peak numbers are reached, Malahide and Rogerstown estuaries then hold a total of 400, the North Bull and Baldoyle Bay together 300. There are increases to 100 to 200 in Bannow Bay and in Dungarvan Harbour. There is some decrease in the Tralee Bay and Castlemaine Harbour numbers in Co. Kerry. Usually the Sligo Bay numbers drop slightly in January and in Trawbreaga Bay a slight increase is noticed.

The overall picture leaves an apparent decrease of about 1,000 birds in mid-January as compared with mid-November. The position remains to be clarified.

There are a number of resorts on the west coast where between 50 and 100 winter; these numbers remain constant.

To Co. Cork this goose is a straggler only.

There are several records of inland occurrences, most often of single birds, but once of a flock of thirteen in Co. Kildare in April.

The first arrive in Tralee Bay, Co. Kerry, very regularly between August 27th and September 4th; numbers increase gradually but then rapidly from the end of September and in October. In Wexford Harbour Brent have been known to arrive in early September, but they usually appear in early October. To Strangford Lough it comes in early October, but in Dublin Bay not before the end of October; the few that are seen there at the end of September pass on. In Dungarvan Harbour it has been reported on October 3rd, but usually Brent arrive there later in that month.

Departure is in April; some remain into May; there are two records each for June and July, one for August 6th.

Barnacle Goose: *Branta leucopsis*

Winter visitor.

The estimated population in Ireland in March 1961 was 4,150. The chief haunts of the Barnacle Goose are on the west coast. At least 300 birds are found scattered on islands off the Donegal coast. Lissadell, Co. Sligo, began to be populated at the end of last century: numbers gradually increased and before 1950 about 1,000 were regularly present. Since 1957 only 150 to 200 have wintered there, but about 150 now do so on Inishmurray.

The chief Irish haunt is on the Inishkeas off Co. Mayo, where the population is about 2,500. Elsewhere off Mayo, Galway and Clare some twelve islands have populations of from 50 to 300. On the North Slob, Co. Wexford, numbers have declined; they now seldom exceed 100 birds and these have normally left before the end of February. Maximum numbers on the North Slob were recorded on February 5th 1956 (500), January 26th 1958 (over 300), December 26th 1958 (over 500); on Sheep Island and the adjacent Antrim coast 50 to 100 winter.

In 1961 flocks of 34 and 85 were reported in Co. Kerry in Tralee Bay and on Beginish respectively.

Inland records are for Offaly, Westmeath, Longford, Galway,

Fermanagh and Armagh; in three cases of flocks of eight, eleven and seventeen.

There are September records but most Barnacles arrive about October 20th and depart about April 20th; there are stragglers in May, once on 22nd.

Ringing results show that Barnacles in Ireland are of Greenland stock.

Canada Goose: *Branta canadensis*

Vagrant.

The typical form *Branta c. canadensis* has been recorded at intervals. There were ten or more occurrences before 1900; all were suspected of being birds of introduced stock. None was then recorded until 1954. While from 1954 the occurrences may include some birds of semi-feral stock, the majority are almost certainly genuine vagrants. In most cases the birds have arrived on the Wexford slobs in November at the time of arrival of the bulk of White-fronted Geese and have wintered. Eleven such records relate to single birds; in two instances there were two; once a party of four, once of eight.

Inland, single birds, in company of White-fronted Geese, have been reported thrice (October 31st, February 11th, March 16th), in two cases in the Shannon valley in Offaly, once at Lough Kinale, Co. Longford.

Two 'Lesser Canada Geese' of either the race *Branta c. parvipes* or *Branta c. taverneri* wintered on the North Slob, Co. Wexford, in 1960–61, 1961–62, and one in 1962–63, 1963–64.

Mute Swan: *Cygnus olor*

Resident.

The Mute Swan breeds in every county, its range extending to the west coast and the marine islands of Achill, Inishkea and Inishbofin.

Flocks of fifty or more non-breeding birds are common on tidal waters; one of 400 has been reported in July. Over 100 that summer at the Galway docks depart in September and return in April. There are local movements within the country.

Flocks of considerable strength frequent tidal and large inland waters in winter. The largest assemblies occur in Co. Wexford where up to 500 together are frequent and there are a number of records of from 600 to 950, one of 1,500 birds.

Whooper Swan: *Cygnus cygnus*

Winter visitor. A few remain in summer.

Nowadays this swan is more numerous and more widespread than Bewick's Swan. Whoopers show a marked preference for shallow waters in all provinces and in particular the turloughs of Connacht. On these parties are generally of ten to twenty birds, or less; on favoured waters assemblies of 100 or more birds are found. The largest numbers have been reported at Lough Beg, Co. Derry, where in each of six years over 300 were counted, the maximum being 450, in December. Rahasane turlough, Co. Galway, normally holds 100 or more, 140 having been seen. In Co. Donegal 200 to 300 winter near Inch in Lough Swilly; near Doonbeg, Co. Clare, 150 and 203 have been counted in different years. On the River Shannon near Athlone 100 to 150 are found regularly. At Egginton, Lough Foyle, Co. Derry, 522 were counted on November 4th 1965.

Sea loughs are less frequented, though 219 in a flock were on Strangford Lough in February 1959.

Before 1952 Whooper Swans were seldom seen in Co. Cork, but since then have been coming increasingly.

Up to about 1900 arrival was exceptional before December; nowadays the first Whooper Swans appear in mid-October and there are records for September 4th, 28th, 30th and October 7th. On October 9th 1964 a total of 58 were seen arriving over the sea at Malin Head, Co. Donegal.

Both adult and immature birds are increasingly reported in June, July and August. Usually the birds are single, but quite often three or four are together.

A *pullus* ringed in Iceland on August 15th was recovered the following December in Co. Down.

Bewick's Swan: *Cygnus bewickii*

Winter visitor. Occasional in summer.

This species is a winter visitor to all provinces. It is local in distribution and large assemblies are found regularly in only two places—Rahasane turlough, Co. Galway, at their peak period, namely end December to early March, 150 to 300; on one occasion a single flock of 130 birds: the Rivers Shannon and Brosna where they meet in Co. Offaly, 100 to 150. At Lough Neagh from 100 to over 400 have been seen in the early months of the year.

In a period of severe weather 200 were on the River Shannon near Athlone; in the same period 300 at Donnybrewer, Co. Derry. In another severe period 250 were seen on the River Brosna.

In several places where formerly there were considerable numbers few are now seen; such include Lough Gill, Co. Kerry, Keel Lough, Termoncarragh Lake and Cross Lough, Co. Mayo. In Wexford numbers have diminished and the haunt at the Cull has been drained. The maximum that had been seen at the Cull was between 270 and 280, in 1956.

Bewick's Swan is seen from early November to the end of March; there are isolated records for September and October and a number for April and May. There are six reports, concerning nine birds, in June. In one case a bird remained throughout June, in another two stayed all June and July. There is a further July record.

Griffon Vulture: *Gyps fulvus*

One record.

A young bird, fully grown and in perfect plumage, was captured near Cork Harbour in the spring of 1843.

Golden Eagle: *Aquila chrysaëtos*

Formerly resident. Vagrant.

The Golden Eagle bred extensively in Munster, Connacht and Ulster up to the middle of last century. At the beginning of the present century only a few remained in Donegal and Mayo. In Donegal breeding ceased in 1910, in Mayo about 1912. Non-breeding individuals were occasionally recorded in these counties until 1926 and 1923 respectively, and in Co. Antrim from 1926 to 1930. Since then vagrants have been reported on about seven occasions in the north of the country. In addition, a pair nested successively on the Antrim coast from 1953 to 1960, but without success in 1956.

Spotted Eagle: *Aquila clanga*

One record of two birds.

In January 1845 two Spotted Eagles were shot near Youghal, Co. Cork. Both had been in the district for several weeks. One of them, an immature bird, in the National Museum, Dublin, was critically examined in March 1958 and found referable to *Aquila clanga*.

Buzzard: *Buteo buteo*

Scarce resident and vagrant.

The Buzzard was resident in Ulster until almost exterminated between 1880 and 1890.

In Co. Antrim a pair bred in 1933 and attempted to do so in 1934. In 1953 four pairs were breeding, three of them on Rathlin Island. From 1954 ten pairs bred but when myxomatosis decimated the rabbits numbers declined and in 1961 only one pair was breeding; in 1964 it is doubtful that any was doing so.

In the years before breeding was re-established the Buzzard was a widespread vagrant. From about 1954 when Buzzards were breeding in Antrim reports of birds were widespread in Ulster outside the breeding season; there are records from Cork, Tipperary, Waterford, Wexford, Wicklow, Carlow, Dublin and Galway. A proportion of these occurrences have undoubtedly been of birds from overseas. It is now rarely seen and none has been recorded at Great Saltee in recent years where formerly there were a number of records of single birds in March, April and August to November.

Rough-legged Buzzard: *Buteo lagopus*

Vagrant.

There have been about twenty-six occurrences; all were of single birds except in two cases when two were together.

Records have been between September 5th and February 10th and in the counties Cork (1), Wicklow (8 or more), Kildare (1), Dublin (2), Galway (2), Down (4 or 5), Derry (3), Donegal (2), Tyrone (2), Fermanagh (1).

Sparrowhawk: *Accipiter nisus*

Resident. Probable passage migrant. Probable winter visitor.

Sparrowhawks breed in every county wherever there is sufficient cover. On the Mullet, Co. Mayo, they nest on bushes about ten feet above the ground, or even lower ones in the Bog of Erris.

There is some evidence of passage on the Mayo coast in September and October and of a steady passage in Connemara in August and September. Sparrowhawks have been recorded regularly at Great Saltee from March to May and August to November.

One ringed in Holland in October was recovered in the following January in Co. Monaghan.

In recent years there appears to have been a decrease in the eastern counties and birds were seldom recorded at Saltee.

Goshawk: *Accipiter gentilis*

Nine or ten records.

Accipiter g. gentilis

One was obtained in Co. Wicklow in 1844; one in Co. Longford in 1846. One seen at Lough Beg, Antrim/Derry, August 12th 1956, was perhaps the same bird as one seen there on September 16th. One was seen at Duncrue Street marsh, Co. Antrim, October 1st 1956. An adult was identified at Blennerville, Co. Kerry, on August 7th 1959.

The American Goshawk (*Accipiter g. atricapillus*) has been obtained four times: an adult male in Co. Tipperary in February 1870; a female soon afterwards near Birr, Co. Offaly; an adult male in Co. Tyrone on February 4th 1919; an adult female in Co. Galway on December 23rd 1935.

Kite: *Milvus milvus*

Two or three records.

One in the National Museum was formerly in the Blake-Knox collection and had been obtained near Kilcoole, Co. Wicklow, in November (year not specified). One was seen at Slane, Co. Meath, on November 15th 1951, and one, possibly the same bird, near Miltown, Co. Down, on December 17th.

White-tailed Eagle: *Haliaëtus albicilla*
Formerly resident; since then four records.

This eagle which formerly bred in Munster, Connacht and Ulster and in the Wicklow mountains was by 1900 confined to Kerry and Mayo. Breeding ceased a few years later, since when it has been recorded as follows: a female was shot on Clare Island, Co. Mayo, on November 27th 1935; a juvenile was found dead near Durrow, Co. Leix, in early March 1937; an immature bird was shot near Gort, Co. Galway, in December 1944; an adult was present on Great Skellig, Co. Kerry, from January 9th to 11th 1946.

Honey Buzzard: *Pernis apivoris*
Vagrant.

There have been twenty-two occurrences: except for two cases when two were together, all have been of single birds.

Dated records have fallen between early April and November 15th with a marked preponderance in June.

Recorded in Tipperary (1), Waterford (1), Wexford (4), Carlow (1), Wicklow (1), Kildare (1), Westmeath (1), Leix (1), Offaly (1) (not two, as given in *Birds of Ireland* (1954), p. 107), Louth (1), Down (2), Armagh (1), Antrim (4), Monaghan (1), Tyrone (1).

None was recorded after July 1947, until two were shot in 1965.

Marsh Harrier: *Circus aeruginosus*
Formerly resident. Vagrant.

By 1840 this previously widespread resident had been reduced to a few pairs in the midlands and west. By 1917 none was breeding though non-breeding birds lingered on in favoured haunts until about 1935.

Since 1941 the species has been recorded about every second year, reports being of one, sometimes two and twice three in a year. Eastern coastal counties have been most favoured. Records range from September 1st through each month to May 19th. One was seen in June, another in August. Single birds are known to have remained from January to March and throughout March and April.

Hen Harrier: *Circus cyaneus*

Resident. Possibly winter visitor.

The Hen Harrier never became extinct as a breeding species in Ireland (as was supposed). Numbers had declined until early in the present century the existence of the bird was precarious.

Before 1950 the position was improving and continues to do so. Breeding is now known to take place in six counties. The number nesting in 1964 was at least thirty-five pairs. There is a marked preference for afforested areas where the trees are not too high and are mixed with a strong growth of gorse, *Ulex gallii*, the plantations being situated on rolling moorland usually on an Old Red Sandstone base.

One ringed as a nestling in Orkney in July 1962 was shot in Co. Offaly in December 1962.

Following the breeding season, Hen Harriers disperse and are reported widespread in all provinces. The extent of immigration is therefore difficult to assess, but there are records of the bird at Great Saltee, Co. Wexford, in April and May and from October to November, the majority in October. Birds that are perhaps migrants are also reported occasionally at Cape Clear, Co. Cork.

Montagu's Harrier: *Circus pygargus*

Scarce resident. Vagrant or possibly winter visitor.

This harrier was considered to have bred in Co. Wicklow in 1899 and 1919. In another county it nested, probably successfully, in 1955. None was found anywhere in 1956, but in 1957 and 1958 a pair bred in yet another county and elsewhere in 1959. The breeding of one or perhaps two pairs probably continues.

Records in the months April to August may have had some connection with breeding. Birds have been recorded at Great Saltee and also in widely separated counties in September and October. There is only one winter record of the species.

Osprey: *Pandion haliaëtus*

Irregular visitor, chiefly in autumn.

There are seventy-seven records, in almost every instance of one bird. The Osprey is less frequently reported than it was in the last century. It has occurred most frequently in Kerry and Cork, but with records on both coastal and inland waters in twenty-one counties.

September and October provide the majority of instances. January and December are alone without record.

In 1962 one was present from May 13th to 23rd in Luska Bay, Lough Derg, Co. Tipperary. In 1965 two were reported, one in May in Co. Cork, the other in July in Co. Armagh.

Hobby: *Falco subbuteo*

Vagrant.

The records of the Hobby number about twenty. Most are for May and June; there are two for both August and September, one for October.

The bird has been reported in Cork, Kerry, Tipperary, Waterford, Dublin, Leitrim, Fermanagh and Down and a marked majority in Wexford.

Peregrine: *Falco peregrinus*

Resident. Probably winter visitor.

Peregrines breed in most maritime counties, on many marine islands and in certain inland mountain ranges where steep crags are available.

About 1950 one hundred and ninety breeding pairs were estimated; the bird was believed to be increasing. There has recently been a serious decline in numbers. It is estimated that the breeding population has fallen to less than seventy pairs and breeding has ceased in some counties. The breeding population along the south coast has drastically decreased.

Out of the breeding season Peregrines range over the countryside far from their breeding areas, often frequenting in autumn and winter the haunts of duck and waders.

A Peregrine was killed against Fastnet lighthouse, Co. Cork, on September 18th; one ringed as a young bird in Scotland in June was found in Co. Wexford the following January.

The bird has occurred, usually singly, at Great Saltee, Co. Wexford, quite often in spring, more frequently in autumn. It is recorded annually at Cape Clear, Co. Cork, in September and October, less often in spring. Although such occurrences are significant, it is hard to know whether they are of genuine migrants or of dispersed breeding stock.

Gyr Falcon: *Falco rusticolus*

The nominate race *Falco r. rusticolus* has never been specifically identified in Ireland.

Greenland Falcon: *Falco r. candicans*

Formerly occasional visitor. Since 1950 only three records.

Up to 1950 sixty had been obtained. Most were in Connacht (22) and Ulster (22), many fewer in Munster (12) and only four in Leinster. In addition, there were sight records of eighteen birds, but with no certainty that they were of this race.

Since 1950 there have been three records: one seen on Tory Island, Co. Donegal, in February and March 1955; one seen in Co. Antrim on October 12th 1957 (both were probably of this race); an adult female was shot in Galway about November 20th 1956.

The majority have been reported in March (13), November (11), April and December (10 each) and one to three in all other months except July and August for which there is no record.

As is now customary in the case of sight records, these have been recorded under the specific name Gyr Falcon, *Falco rusticolus*.

In some years in the past more were reported than in others, thus three winters were notable for reports of eight, ten and eleven birds obtained.

Iceland Falcon, *Falco r. islandus*

Five records.

An immature female was shot in Co. Donegal in September 1859. One was shot at Termoncarragh, near Belmullet, Co. Mayo, in September 1877. One was obtained near Westport, Co. Mayo, in 1883. An immature female obtained at Oughterard, Co. Galway, in 1905 was accompanied by another. One was obtained on Inishtrahull, Co. Donegal, in April 1917.

Merlin: *Falco columbarius*

Resident. Probably winter visitor.

As a breeding bird the Merlin is widely but thinly distributed on high moorland, mountains and some extensive bogs.

After breeding Merlins disperse to the lowlands and coasts. It is thought to have decreased during the present century, but numbers are hard to assess because of its habits, the lonely nature of its haunts and the ease with which it is overlooked in its breeding places.

To what extent it is a winter visitor is uncertain.

The Iceland Merlin (*Falco subaesalon*) is a winter visitor and specimens referable to this form have been obtained in the months August to April, the majority in October. Amongst these are birds from isolated islands, light-stations and reports from Great Saltee in autumn.

One ringed when young in Iceland in June was found in Co. Offaly the following December.

Red-footed Falcon: *Falco vespertinus*

One record.

An adult male was shot in Co. Wicklow in the summer of 1832: the specimen is in the National Museum.

Lesser Kestrel: *Falco naumanni*

One record.

An adult male was shot near Shankill, Co. Dublin, on February 17th 1891: it had been in the locality since early November 1890. The specimen is in the National Museum.

Kestrel: *Falco tinnunculus*

Resident. Autumn emigrant and/or passage migrant. Winter visitor.

Kestrels breed in every county and on many marine islands. They are scattered rather thinly and are nowhere numerous. Evidence points to a recent local decrease which in some parts of eastern Ireland is appreciable.

There is some migration within the country: in Ulster Kestrels become less numerous in winter. Elsewhere the numbers in coastal areas increase.

In autumn birds have been noticed flying out to sea, going south-east from Carnsore Point and Great Saltee, Co. Wexford, and flying south-west from Cape Clear, Co. Cork. An adult ringed at Saltee while on migration on September 9th was recovered the following December in Wales. There is migration through Saltee from August to November, chiefly in September. On two occasions in autumn specimens have been obtained at lighthouses. A nestling ringed in Norway in June was shot in Co. Kerry the following October, another ringed in Scotland was found in the following autumn in Co. Down. It is not possible to say whether any of these records are of emigrants or of passage migrants.

Kestrels appear at Saltee irregularly from March to May and specimens have twice been obtained in spring at light-stations.

Red Grouse: *Lagopus lagopus*

Resident.

The Irish Red Grouse, *Lagopus l. hibernicus*, is a sub-species peculiar to Ireland (and the Hebrides).

Birds and eggs of the British race, *L. l. scoticus*, have been frequently and widely introduced. Despite this, no apparent change in the characteristics of the true *hibernicus* is considered to have taken place.

The Grouse is sparsely distributed except where locally preserved. There has been a marked decrease in the present century and a serious one in the past few years except in some counties in Ulster where conservation is much more efficacious.

Capercaillie: *Tetrao urogallus*
Extinct.

Capercaillie were formerly abundant in the natural forests of Ireland but gradually decreased and became extinct before 1800.

Partridge: *Perdix perdix*
Resident.

Sparsely distributed, chiefly in cultivated districts, but sometimes found in the small cultivated fields in desolate areas.

The introduction of fresh stocks and protective legislation in 1930 stemmed the decline in numbers: the bird has since become more numerous in grain-growing counties.

Quail: *Coturnix coturnix*
Summer visitor.

The Quail was resident and abundant up to about 1850. It then became scarce, but in 1893 again became more numerous and appeared irregularly in many localities and breeding was reported here and there. Since about 1940 it has bred with some regularity in Co. Carlow and does so annually in Co. Kildare. There have been reports of breeding in Antrim, Dublin, Offaly and Galway.

Quail have been reported without evidence of breeding in Kerry, Cork, Waterford, Wexford, Tipperary, Wicklow, Louth, Meath, Tyrone and Down. The numbers reported show that its visits are still given to fluctuation. Rather more than average were reported in 1964.

After the breeding season the birds depart but in 1953 one was reported in January in Co. Waterford. One remained into November in Co. Kildare in 1961 and a whole brood wintered there in 1962–63.

Pheasant: *Phasianus colchicus*
Resident.

The Pheasant *Ph. c. colchicus* was introduced about 1589 and now breeds in every county.

Photo: Irish Tourist Board

TYPICAL BREEDING TERRAIN OF THE HEN HARRIER

Photo: Irish Tourist Board

CORNCRAKE COUNTRY, WESTERN CONNACHT

The Chinese Ring-necked Pheasant *Ph. c. torquatus* was later introduced; the two races have interbred. Most birds are hybrids nowadays. Re-stocking is taking place on quite an extensive scale and the population is increasing.

Crane: *Megalornis grus*
Vagrant.

The Crane was abundant in Ireland in the Middle Ages. This statement has been supported by the finding of numerous remains of the bird in caves and lake dwellings.

Since 1809 it has been reported fifteen times at widely separated intervals. Since 1950 only three have been recorded.

Single birds have been the more usual, but two, three, five and once six or seven together have been seen: the last remained in Co. Kerry for four or five months from October 1940.

Occurrences have taken place in Kerry (4), Cork (2), Wexford (1), Tipperary (1), Offaly (1), Galway (1), Mayo (1), Down (1), Derry (1), Donegal (2). The months where known have been January (2), May (1), June (2), July (1), September (1), October (1), November (2), December (1).

Sandhill Crane: *Megalornis canadensis*
One record.

One was shot near the coast in Co. Cork on September 14th 1905. All the facts point to its having been a genuine wild bird. The specimen is in the National Museum.

Water Rail: *Rallus aquaticus*
Resident. Passage migrant. Winter visitor.

The nominate form *Rallus a. aquaticus* is resident and found in suitable habitat throughout the country. It breeds in every county and on Clare Island and Rathlin Island.

Water Rails killed at lighthouses while on migration have been critically examined and found to be of the nominate form, thus indicating an autumn immigration.

The Water Rail of Iceland *Rallus a. hibernans* is a winter visitor and probably a passage migrant also; specimens critically examined support this view.

The Continental form *Rallus a.? germanicus* (a name not yet officially assigned to the race) is represented by specimens from light-stations which indicate that the bird is a winter visitor and/or a passage migrant in autumn.

Although not possible to assess them all as to race, there is a heavy migration of Water Rails on the east and west coasts in autumn and chiefly on the east coast in spring.

It is likely that the numerous migrants on the west coast, especially those at Tory Island, are of Icelandic origin, the east coast ones being of British and Continental stock, as evidence of which there are some specimens.

Spotted Crake: *Porzana porzana*

Has bred. Vagrant.

The Spotted Crake is known to have bred once, about 1851, in Co. Roscommon. It probably bred more than the once and was thought to have bred in Leix, Louth and Fermanagh at that period, when it was evidently not uncommon in summer.

There are about eighty records, chiefly from August to October, sixty of them since 1900. There are single records for the months January to April, two for May, five for November, three for December.

Reports nowadays are chiefly of single birds killed at lighthouses.

Most records are for Munster, least for Connacht.

Sora Rail: *Porzana carolina*

One record.

An adult male was killed at Slyne Head lighthouse, Co. Galway, on April 11th 1920.

A few months before, an immature bird had been captured at sea 100 miles off the west coast of Ireland.

Baillon's Crake: *Porzana pusilla*
Two records.

One was killed on October 30th 1845 near Youghal, Co. Cork. One was caught on April 6th 1858 near Tramore, Co. Waterford.

Little Crake: *Porzana parva*
Three records.

A male was shot on March 11th 1854 at Balbriggan, Co. Dublin, and one on November 12th 1903 in Co. Offaly. One was seen on Cape Clear Island, Co. Cork, on April 14th 1964.

Corncrake: *Crex crex*
Summer visitor. Passage migrant. Occasionally in winter.

The Corncrake, formerly so widespread and numerous, has decreased in numbers enormously. Corncrakes are still not uncommon west of the River Shannon and locally elsewhere but generally relatively few are now found except in the extreme west, north-west and south-west, where in places on the seaboard and particularly on some marine islands they are still numerous. Even on Cape Clear Island, Co. Cork, a decline in breeding pairs has been noted.

Summer visitors and probably passage migrants begin to arrive on the south coast in April; some depart in August, most have left by the end of September or early October. Instances of birds in the months November to March have been reported in each province.

Moorhen: *Gallinula chloropus*
Resident. Probable passage migrant. Winter visitor.

The Waterhen, by which name it is more generally known in Ireland, breeds in every county and on marine islands. In western regions it is locally scarce or absent.

There is migration on the east coast in March and April and on both east and west coasts in September and October, sometimes in

November. These movements are perhaps of passage migrants as no marked increased in winter numbers is noticed. Some do come as winter visitors as one ringed in Scotland in September and a juvenile ringed in Denmark were both recovered in the November following ringing.

Coot: *Fulica atra*

Resident. Winter visitor.

The Coot breeds in every county. It is scarce in western Donegal, but in Connemara is widespread. It breeds on some marine islands.

In June flocks of non-breeding birds occur; up to 150 Coots together have been seen in mid-June.

Migration is noticed on the coast from September to November, almost exclusively on the east coast.

Numbers increase in winter: flocks of over a hundred birds are common on inland and quiet coastal waters. In favoured haunts 500 or more are seen; 1,500 together have been reported in October.

Considerable weather movement is sometimes noticed in January.

Coots ringed in England and Denmark have been recovered in Ireland in winter. A juvenile ringed in June in Co. Down had moved to Scotland by December.

Great Bustard: *Otis tarda*

Two records.

Two were seen near Thurles, Co. Tipperary, in December 1902; one of them, a female, was obtained. A female was shot near Castletownbere, Co. Cork, on December 9th 1925.

Little Bustard: *Otis tetrax*

Eight records.

One was shot on December 30th 1892 near Ballybunion, Co. Kerry. In Co. Cork one was killed on December 24th 1860 at Ballycotton Bay; one near Ballymacoda on November 14th 1883. Two were seen and one of them shot at Killough, Co. Wicklow, on August 23rd 1833. One was shot in Co. Longford in February 1883.

Of two seen near Belmullet, Co. Mayo, in December 1887 one was shot. One was shot near Ennis, Co. Clare, on December 20th 1916. One was shot on or about November 19th 1931 at Skerries, Co. Dublin.

It is doubtful whether specimens were ever critically examined as to race. None can now be traced.

Oystercatcher: *Haematopus ostralegus*

Resident. Winter visitor.

The Oystercatcher breeds numerously, chiefly on marine islands, especially in the north and west. In recent years it has been nesting on the mainland in Wexford, Wicklow, Waterford and Louth, but it rarely nests on mainland shingle-beaches.

In some places nests are found at a little distance from the coast-line. Far inland it has nested on Lough Erne, and does so on Lough Neagh and at Lough Beg in Co. Derry. It has probably bred on Lough Arrow in Co. Sligo, but proof is lacking.

Many non-breeding birds are seen in summer and flocks of up to 70 have been reported. In Belfast Lough flocks of up to 500 birds are normal in July and on the North Bull, Co. Dublin, about 2,000 in a loose flock is commonplace in July.

At times of migration, especially in autumn, Oystercatchers are seen at or passing over inland waters, even in the very interior of the country. Usually the birds are single but flocks of up to ten and once fifteen birds have been reported.

From autumn to spring very large flocks frequent the coasts. Many of these birds are immigrants from Iceland, the Faeroes and Scotland. It is most improbable that any come from the Continent.

Migration in autumn is chiefly noticed on the west and north coasts.

A full-grown bird colour-ringed in Devon in October 1960 and recaught there in October 1962 was found nesting at Great Saltee in 1963.

Sociable Plover: *Chettusia gregaria*

Two records.

A female was obtained on August 1st 1889 near Navan, Co.

Meath. One was shot about December 25th 1909 near Brownstown Head, Tramore Bay, Co. Waterford; it is in the National Museum.

Lapwing: *Vanellus vanellus*

Resident. Passage migrant. Winter visitor.

Lapwings breed in every county and on many of the marine islands. As a breeding species it has decreased. Only a very few breed locally in Co. Cork.

Nesting rarely takes place on arable land, but has been recorded in Co. Dublin in growing wheat. Irish bred birds are mainly sedentary or subject to local movements.

In spring there is passage migration and return of those which may have emigrated in winter.

Small flocks begin to form at the end of June and birds from high ground and exposed areas move to the coast.

Numerous immigrants arrive from mid-September, the numbers increasing in October. In severe winters great numbers come from Britain and the Continent.

The earlier arrivals in autumn come from Scotland and the northern half of England. Birds ringed in Denmark, Norway, Sweden and Finland have been recovered widespread.

Flocks of 500 to 1,000 are commonplace at any time in winter. In January and February flocks of 2,000 birds have been seen.

Ringed Plover: *Charadrius hiaticula*

Resident. Passage migrant. Winter visitor.

Ringed Plover breed in the maritime counties, except in Leitrim, on many marine islands, at the larger inland lakes and sometimes at quite small ones.

Birds arrive on their nesting grounds from mid-February to mid-April and leave again about the end of July. Flocks then appear on the coast, juvenile birds being in the majority.

Inland passage is very noticeable, especially on the Connacht lakes during August, with fewer moving in September and October.

In winter, though seldom seen far inland, Ringed Plover are abundant on the coasts, the resident birds having been augmented by autumn immigrants. Flocks of 200 to 300 are not unusual and of 100 to 200 frequent. Some home-bred birds leave the country in their first autumn.

The Arctic Ringed Plover (*Charadrius h. tundrae*) is a passage migrant and probably a winter visitor.

Ten specimens in the National Museum are referable to this race. They are from all coasts and were obtained in the months August to October, February and April to June. Examples have been handled in April and August at Tory Island, Co. Donegal; in August and September at Rathlin Island, Co. Antrim; one at Great Saltee, Co. Wexford, in September. Many of the Ringed Plover that arrived at Malin Head, Co. Donegal, on October 2nd and 3rd 1963 had the characteristics of this race.

Little Ringed Plover: *Charadrius dubius*

One record of four birds.

On September 17th 1953 a party of four was seen on the North Bull strand, Co. Dublin.

Kentish Plover: *Charadrius alexandrinus*

Eight records.

In Co. Dublin one was shot on the North Bull probably in the autumn of 1846; one was shot at Baldoyle on August 8th 1848; an adult male was killed near Clontarf in August 1851; one was seen at Dun Laoghaire on August 18th and 19th 1948. In Co. Antrim one was seen at Lough Neagh on October 18th 1959; one was seen at Duncrue Street marsh, Belfast, on August 2nd 1960. In Co. Down one was seen at Kinnegar on August 16th 1960. One was seen on Lough Neagh, Co. Antrim, October 7th 1964.

There were several unsatisfactory records in 1848 and 1852.

Kildeer: *Charadrius vociferus*

Five records.

An adult male was shot at Naul, near Balbriggan, Co. Dublin, on January 12th 1928. One was shot near Crookhaven, Co. Cork, on November 30th 1938 and one was picked up dead near Crookhaven on March 19th 1939. One was seen at Akeagh Lough, Co. Kerry, on February 26th 1958; it remained until March 2nd. One was present near Annagh Island in Tralee Bay, Co. Kerry, from at least November 20th to December 2nd 1958.

Grey Plover: *Charadrius squatarola*

Probable passage migrant in autumn. Winter visitor. Occasional in summer and inland.

The little clear evidence of passage migration is for the autumn.

The Grey Plover is found on all coasts but less numerously on those of the south-west and west; on those of Clare and Galway it is scarce.

Grey Plover are present from mid-September until March, occasionally in August and later than March. There are about twenty records of individuals or small parties in the months June to August. Most often it is seen singly or in twos and threes, less often in numbers up to twenty; loose flocks of 56 and 80 have been reported and there are records of compact flocks of 68, 100 and 120 to 130.

Birds in summer plumage are frequently seen in late spring and early autumn; most of those seen in the summer months have been in winter plumage.

Inland the Grey Plover is a vagrant or passage migrant, rarely in spring, more often in autumn. Nowadays at Lough Beg, Co. Derry, it occurs every autumn; as many as thirty-three birds together have been seen there. Other inland records in autumn come from the Shannon valley, the Connacht lakes and other inland waters. In November thirty-five were seen near Craughwell, Co. Galway.

Single birds have been seen in November in Co. Westmeath and in December near Craughwell, Co. Galway, and near Athlone.

Golden Plover: *Charadrius apricarius*

Resident. Passage migrant. Winter visitor.

The race *Charadrius a. apricarius* breeds in small and greatly decreased numbers. It nests sparsely only on some mountains in

Galway, Mayo, Cavan, Antrim, Fermanagh and perhaps in Donegal. In Connemara, Co. Galway and in western Mayo a few nest locally on moors only slightly above sea level.

Among the breeding stock are found some birds showing the characteristics of the Northern race, but lacking black on the forehead. Such birds are best referred to as 'near-*altifrons* type'.

It is impossible to say what proportion of the numerous wintering Golden Plover are of this race. Ringing recoveries indicate that very few, if any, are immigrants from the Continent.

The Northern Golden Plover (*Charadrius a. altifrons*) is a recognisable passage migrant from mid-August to early October and in April and May.

Probably the majority of winter visitors are of this race, but as with the typical race it is impossible to know the proportion.

There are numerous cases of birds of this race, ringed as nestlings in Iceland, having been recovered in all the provinces between September and March.

Winter flocks, of whichever race, are of thousands. Callow lands are the favourite habitat, but locally the birds haunt coastal mudflats on which flocks of over 1,000 have been reported. Migrants rarely halt on sandy beaches, but in one case 768 were counted in October.

Lesser Golden Plover: *Charadrius dominicus*

Three records.

An adult was shot on September 13th 1894 at Belmullet, Co. Mayo. One was shot on November 29th 1952 near Kells, Co. Meath. Both are in the National Museum. One in practically full summer plumage was seen on September 15th 1963 on Ballyheigue strand, Co. Kerry, and the same bird at adjacent Lough Akeagh from 19th to 22nd.

Dotterel: *Charadrius morinellus*

Vagrant on passage.

There are records of about twenty-five occurrences which have taken place in Kerry (3), Cork (1), Tipperary (1), Waterford (4),

Wexford (5), Dublin (2), Roscommon (1), Cavan (1), Down (2), Antrim (2), Derry (1) and Donegal (1). In another instance the county is unknown. One or two other reports are omitted due to the existence of doubt.

Though the bird has been found singly, there are reports of several seen together. Parties of twenty, twenty-five and between twenty and thirty have been recorded, in each case in March or April. There have been nearly twice as many occurrences in autumn as in spring.

Birds have sometimes remained in one locality for several days.

A bird ringed at Great Saltee, Co. Wexford, on September 29th 1961 was recovered on June 9th 1962 near Igarka, on the River Yenisei, U.S.S.R.

Turnstone: *Arenaria interpres*

Non-breeding summer visitor. Passage migrant. Winter visitor.

Turnstones are found in the summer months and even in July flocks of from twenty to sixty-five have been reported. Smaller parties are found widespread on all coasts. Many of the July birds are adults in summer plumage.

Turnstones are common on passage and in winter on all suitable coasts.

There is overland passage in spring and autumn which is especially noticeable on the western lakes, on the Shannon lakes and Lough Neagh.

One ringed in Co. Antrim in January 1942 was recovered in north-west Greenland on May 30th 1945.

A full-grown bird ringed in south-west Iceland on May 25th 1961 was recovered in Co. Clare about January 5th 1962.

Short-billed Dowitcher: *Limnodromus griseus*

Two records concerning six birds.

One was seen at Lough Funshinagh, Co. Roscommon, from October 1st to 10th 1963. At Rahasane turlough, Co. Galway, four were seen on October 2nd 1963, a maximum of five on 10th and two on 20th.

Long-billed Dowitcher: *Limnodromus scolopaceus*
Five records.

At least five have been found in Ireland, for some of those given below as indeterminate may have been of this species.

One in the National Museum was received there from Port Laoise (Maryborough), Leix, on September 29th 1893. One was shot in Co. Tipperary about October 9th 1893. One was seen at Akeagh Lough, Co. Kerry, from September 18th to 25th 1960. One was seen at Tory Island, Co. Donegal, on May 5th 1962. One was seen at Akeagh Lough on September 26th 1965.

Indeterminate examples of *L. griseus* or *L. scolopaceus* have been seen as follows:—One on the North Slob, Co. Wexford, on September 29th 1956. One at Kilbarrack, Co. Dublin, on October 19th 1958. One on the salt-marsh at Blennerville, Co. Kerry, on December 3rd 1958. One at Akeagh Lough, Co. Kerry, on October 11th 1960. One at Lough Beg, Co. Derry, on October 28th 1961 and another from October 2nd to 15th 1963.

Snipe: *Capella gallinago*
Resident. Winter visitor.

Snipe breed plentifully in every county and do so on some marine islands such as Achill, Rathlin, Great Saltee and Cape Clear.

Our home-bred Snipe are mainly sedentary, performing dispersal and weather movements, but there is no proof that they leave Ireland.

Immigration commences early in September, and continues in October; November and December are the months of greatest influx. The winter visitors are from England and Scotland; a nestling ringed in Schleswig-Holstein and one from Finland were recovered in winter. The wintering Snipe leave again in March.

The numbers found have declined progressively during the present century.

Specimens of the Faeroe Snipe (*Capella g. faeroeensis*) have been examined from Kildare, Mayo, Donegal and Tyrone and there have been widespread recoveries in winter of nestlings ringed in Iceland.

This race is a winter visitor from October until February.

The so-called 'Sabine's Snipe' is a well-defined melanistic variety which has not been reported since 1909, though previous to that year there were about fifty records covering seventeen counties, but few of them in the east.

Many hundreds of Snipe have been carefully examined without ever finding one of the North American race, *Gallinago g. delicata.*

Great Snipe: *Capella media*

Vagrant.

There are about eighteen records of which one was at the end of February, the remainder in the months September to December. Occurrences have taken place in Cork (1), Wexford (3 or more), Kildare (3), Dublin (1), Meath (1), Galway (2), Mayo (2), Leitrim (2), Tyrone (1), Antrim (2).

Twelve were shot between 1827 and 1899; since 1900 only six have been recorded, the last being one seen at Great Saltee in September 1957.

Jack Snipe: *Lymnocryptes minimus*

Passage migrant. Winter visitor.

This snipe is widely distributed but extremely local. Usually the Jack Snipe is encountered singly or in twos or threes, rarely eight or ten have been flushed from a restricted area of ground.

Immigrants arrive chiefly in October and November, sometimes in August and September. Departure takes place in March, April or even May. On June 24th 1954 one was seen in Co. Kerry.

Woodcock: *Scolopax rusticola*

Resident. Partial migrant. Winter visitor.

Woodcock now breed in every county; the spread on a large scale commenced in 1833.

The majority of Irish-bred Woodcock are sedentary, but dispersal takes place after the breeding season and there is much local weather movement and some emigration.

Young ringed in Ireland have travelled to England, Scotland, France, Spain and Portugal; one was recovered in Sweden seven years after being ringed in Co. Tyrone.

There is a large immigration from October onwards, birds coming from Britain and the Continent. From December to February weather movements take place, fresh immigrants arriving. Numbers wintering fluctuate from year to year and also from month to month.

For a period about the middle of this century Woodcock were not so abundant in winter as formerly. With the great increase of conifer plantations there is now widespread cover. While the birds are not so concentrated as in the days of the large estates, it is believed that the total population has increased in recent years, at least locally.

In the last century 1,250 Woodcock were shot in one winter in Co. Kerry. At Ashford, Co. Galway, 165 were shot in one day and larger bags were of 172 and 178 in subsequent years. In 1944 at Ashford 131 were shot in two days; on January 2nd 1945, 87 in Co. Roscommon and on 4th 56 in Co. Longford. All these were considered above present-day average.

Upland Plover: *Bartramia longicauda*

Four records.

One was received in Dublin from Ballinasloe, Co. Galway, in the autumn of 1885. One was shot on September 4th 1894 at Newcestown, Co. Cork. One was shot in November, probably 1901, at Bunduff, Co. Sligo. One was seen on the North Slob, Co. Wexford, on September 29th and 30th 1956.

Curlew: *Numenius arquata*

Resident. Winter visitor.

Curlew breed in every county but in many sparsely or very locally. In Donegal few breed. The most favoured breeding haunts are the callow lands, particularly those in the Shannon valley, marshy and badly tended ground, the great flat bogs and in a less degree high moorland.

During summer non-breeding birds are found on the coasts of every province.

After the breeding season numbers on the coasts increase. Winter visitors arrive in September, but the majority from mid-October to mid-November; they leave again in March and April.

Ringing results show that immigrants come from Scotland and northern England and from Norway, Sweden, Finland and Holland.

Coastal flocks are sometimes composed of several thousand birds; large flocks are frequent far inland, especially in western regions, and these sometimes contain 1,000 birds or more.

From July to March Curlew habitually roost at regular sites; such inland roosts are occupied by anything from 80 to 1,500 birds

Whimbrel: *Numenius phaeopus*

Passage migrant. Occasional in summer and winter.

More Whimbrel pass through Ireland on spring than on autumn passage. Passage takes place on all coasts and inland, especially through Connacht. Spring passage is regular from mid-April to mid-June, though individuals are reported rarely at the end of March and not infrequently in early April. There are a few records for late June.

One summered in Tralee Bay, Co. Kerry, in each of the three years 1955 to 1957, at least fifteen did so in 1958 and at least ten in 1960, four in 1962.

Autumn passage often commences in July: it is at its height in August and September and declines in October; stragglers pass until mid-November.

There have been about ten winter records of from one to three birds, ranging from December 12th to February 24th.

Spring migrants form regular inland roosts at which up to a hundred have been counted.

The Hudsonian Whimbrel (*Numenius phaeopus hudsonicus*) has once been reported. One was seen in Tralee Harbour, Co. Kerry, on October 1st 1957.

Eskimo Curlew: *Numenius borealis*

One record.

A specimen of this species, now considered extinct, was found in a Dublin poulterer's shop in October 1870. It had definitely been shot in Ireland, probably in Co. Sligo. The specimen is in the National Museum.

Black-tailed Godwit: *Limosa limosa*

Non-breeding summer visitor. Passage migrant. Winter visitor.

In all probability the Black-tailed Godwits which visit Ireland are of the Icelandic race (*Limosa limosa islandica*). This view is supported by an analysis of specimens in the British Museum (Nat. Hist.) and in the National Museum, Dublin. The former contains no Continental birds taken in Ireland; in the latter only two qualify as the nominate race and then only if they had been correctly sexed.

As a passage migrant and winter visitor this godwit has greatly increased in the past ten years, even before which an increase had been noticed.

There are occurrences for every month and in June and July flocks of 200 have been seen, birds in breeding plumage being fairly frequent.

Due to the summering birds dates of spring and autumn passage cannot be separated. Numbers increase from August onwards and decrease again in April, but are relatively low from December to January and are high in March.

Recent reports of flocks of between 200 and 1,500 are frequent. The following give an idea of numbers to be met with in flocks regularly in the months August to April:—August, 800, 850; September, 400, 600, 1,300; October, over 800; November, 1,500; December, 250, 150; January, 450; February, 220, 450, 500; March, 600, 900, 1,000; April, 200, 350, 521; October, about 1,200. The largest assemblies are found in parts of Co. Wexford, Cork Harbour, the Shannon valley near Banagher and in Co. Limerick. There are many places which have a maximum of only twenty to thirty birds.

Recently there have been flocks at both coastal and inland localities where previously none was found.

Distribution on the coast is irregular. Certain bays and estuaries are regularly tenanted, others similar in appearance of terrain hold none. The size of inland flocks is generally smaller than those on or adjacent to the coast.

Bar-tailed Godwit: *Limosa lapponica*

Passage migrant. Winter visitor. Non-breeding summer visitor.

During the second half of August some Bar-tailed Godwits arrive on the east coast; in early September the immigration is large and not confined to the east coast. Arrivals continue into October.

Returning passage migrants swell the April flocks; in May numbers decline. In the north of the country passage is more evident because relatively few remain in winter.

Distribution on the coasts, though widespread, is irregular as in the case of the Black-tailed Godwit. The two species are not found in the same bays or estuaries other than in very small numbers.

In favoured places flocks are of from 300 to 1,000 birds; 2,000 and over have been reported.

Considerable numbers of this godwit are present in summer, flocks of 40, 50 and even over 80 have been seen in June. On the North Bull, Co. Dublin, about 250 summered in 1958. In recent years birds in summer plumage have frequently been seen.

Inland the Bar-tailed Godwit is unusual, though there is a mounting number of records. On Lough Beg, Co. Derry, it is almost annual in autumn in numbers from one to three, but once ten and once sixteen. Individuals are found irregularly far inland in Connacht.

Green Sandpiper: *Tringa ochropus*

Autumn and winter visitor. Vagrant in spring and summer.

The Green Sandpiper is nowadays an annual visitor, mostly in the months August to March. Some winter in certain localities and are recorded annually. The bird is still infrequent in the months April to July. Since 1950 there are the following records: April (4), May (1), June (2), July (7). One was present in Cork Harbour from April to September 1965. It was joined by a second from July to September.

Photo: Ian Finlay

(A) LOW FLAT MOORLAND, TYPICAL BREEDING HAUNT OF GOLDEN PLOVER

Photo: Ian Finlay

(B) ESTUARINE MARSH

Photo: David Cabot

(A) BALLIN LAKE, CO. WATERFORD. TYPICAL OF MANY WATERFOWL RESORTS THROUGHOUT IRELAND

Photo: Rex Roberts Studios

(B) GREAT SALTEE, CO. WEXFORD, FROM THE SOUTH

Occurrences are well scattered but less frequent west of the River Shannon. In Co. Kerry it is less often seen than the Wood Sandpiper.

It has been recorded in every county except Longford, Leitrim, Cavan and Monaghan. Only since 1953 have Roscommon, Fermanagh, Armagh and Derry been added to the counties where it has been noted.

There are reports of two to four together, but usually of single birds.

Wood Sandpiper: *Tringa glareola*

Autumn passage migrant. Vagrant in spring and summer.

Formerly this bird was a vagrant. None was recorded for the period 1910 to 1949. Up to 1950 only eight occurrences were known. Since then the increase has been real and Wood Sandpipers are recorded annually. In the three years 1960 to 1962 alone forty different birds were reported. There were unusual numbers in 1956 when occurrences took place in Dublin, Wicklow, Kerry, Wexford and Mayo. In 1962 there were more than usual with records in Dublin, Wicklow, Wexford, Armagh, Cork, Derry and Kerry. With the exception of Armagh all records have been in coastal counties.

The following shows the distribution of occurrences: Dublin (18), Kerry (14), Derry (13), Wexford (10), Armagh (7), Wicklow (6), Antrim (7), Mayo (4), Cork (6), Down (4), Waterford, Galway, Donegal two each.

Most have been reported in August and September; there are records for April (1), May (7), June (8), July (5), November (1), December (1).

Up to six birds together have been seen, more usually single birds or two.

Common Sandpiper: *Tringa hypoleucos*

Summer visitor. Occasional in winter.

The bird is a widespread summer visitor. It breeds in every county except Wexford and Kilkenny; it is scarce in other counties in the south-east except when on migration. Common Sandpipers breed on marine islands and are particularly common on the River Shannon and on the large midland and western lakes.

The first arrive about mid-April, more come in May and it then becomes generally distributed. There are early records for March 3rd, April 9th and 11th.

By mid-July breeding grounds become vacated by the majority, the birds then move to coastal areas. Emigration takes place in August and September.

There are about twenty-five records, chiefly of single birds, between November 4th and February 12th, the majority in December and January. For three successive winters one to three birds wintered in Co. Antrim.

The Spotted Sandpiper (*Tringa hypoleucos macularia*) has once been obtained. One was shot near the River Finnea, Co. Westmeath, on February 2nd 1899.

Redshank: *Tringa totanus*

Resident. Passage migrant. Winter visitor.

No example of the nominate race *Tringa totanus totanus* has been identified. It is unlikely that Ireland receives any Redshanks from the Continent (*Brit. Birds*, 56: 234).

The race *Tringa t. britannica* breeds in every county except Carlow, Cork, Waterford, Kilkenny and Kerry. In Kerry a pair bred in 1957 but not again. Only since 1941 has breeding been proved in Wexford, though it was suspected in 1930. Breeding rarely occurs in western Donegal or west of longitude 9°15′W in Galway and Mayo, nor in Clare except near Lahinch and also just west of Ballyeighter Lough and at Carran Lough.

After breeding most Redshanks move to coastal mudflats, returning to their breeding haunts at the end of March.

A few birds ringed when young in Scotland and northern England have been recovered in widely separated counties.

There is a very large immigration of Redshanks in autumn but it is not possible to say in what proportion races are represented in the wintering population. A very large number are probably of the Icelandic race *Tringa t. robusta*. Specimens of this race have been examined from Mayo, Donegal, Antrim, Down and Dublin and one ringed in Iceland was recovered in Galway.

The winter visitors depart between mid-February and mid-April, stragglers remaining into May.

Outside of the breeding season few Redshanks are found far inland, though some flocks of up to ten birds are reported inland each winter.

In autumn and spring there is passage migration when flocks of twenty to fifty are seen inland and there is heavy passage movement on the coasts. The autumn passage sometimes commences in July. In Wexford Harbour 1,000 have been seen on September 19th, 1,500 on October 3rd and rather smaller numbers elsewhere in mid-September.

In winter, at high water, gatherings of hundreds are found in favoured places; elsewhere assemblies of 50 to 150 birds are commonplace.

Spotted Redshank: *Tringa erythropus*

Passage migrant. Winter visitor.

Before 1952 this bird was a vagrant. Up to 1954 there were seventy records mostly of single birds, rarely of two or three together. In 1955 numbers suddenly increased and now the bird is of regular occurrence in autumn, a few remain in winter, some occur on spring passage, especially in April. There are records for every month, the majority for the last quarter of the year. May occurrences are uncommon, June records are very unusual.

The numbers recorded are increasing annually and are widespread, chiefly on or near the coasts and tidal waters in all maritime counties except Meath and Leitrim. Most are seen in Co. Wexford; Akeagh Lough in Co. Kerry is much visited.

Though found annually in the west, it is scarcer there; a flock of eleven in Galway Bay in October 1964 being exceptional. Co. Dublin, whence came the majority of records previous to 1950, is now seldom visited. The Spotted Redshank has been frequently seen in the Shannon valley, on Lough Carra in Co. Mayo and at inland waters in Co. Galway and at Lough Beg, Co. Derry. There are records of it in Kildare, Roscommon and Westmeath.

From 1959 there has been a noticeable increase in the size of flocks, six to eight birds together being frequent. By 1962 larger flocks were being reported: one of nineteen on the North Slob,

Co. Wexford, on September 9th. In 1963 at Blennerville, Co. Kerry, there was a flock of eighteen on September 3rd, on 20th there were twenty-two birds, twenty of them in a flock. In 1965 flocks of over forty and fifty birds were on the South Slob, Co. Wexford on August 29th and October 7th, respectively.

Birds in summer plumage have been noted several times.

Greater Yellowlegs: *Tringa melanoleuca*

Six records.

One was shot on January 21st 1940 at Aghadown, near Skibbereen, Co. Cork. One without data was shot in Ireland and found in fresh condition on January 29th 1947 in a game dealer's store in Dublin City. One was seen on Downpatrick marshes, Co. Down, on December 18th 1955. One was seen at Three Islets, Lough Neagh, Co. Antrim, on September 2nd 1962 and probably the same bird at adjacent Lough Beg on 22nd. One was seen on Bog Meadows, Belfast, Co. Antrim, from April 14th to 16th 1962. One was seen at Tory Island, Co. Donegal, on October 5th 1964.

Lesser Yellowlegs: *Tringa flavipes*

Five records.

There are the following sight records of single birds: Swords estuary, Co. Dublin, April 8th 1961; South Slob channel, Co. Wexford, September 19th 1963; Tacumshin Lake, Co. Wexford, September 11th to 13th 1964; Swords estuary, Co. Dublin, October 25th to December 10th 1964; Tacumshin Lake, May 8th 1965.

Greenshank: *Tringa nebularia*

Passage migrant. Winter visitor.

Greenshanks reappear on our coasts about mid-June, occasionally early in June. Numbers gradually increase and reach their maximum in October and November. Numbers then drop and are smallest in December and January, then increase again markedly in February. By April most have departed. May occurrences are few.

Greenshanks are often found inland.

A juvenile ringed in Scotland in June was recovered in the following October in Co. Cork.

Greenshanks winter regularly and in larger numbers than formerly. A flock of forty-four was seen in Co. Kerry in January and at least 200 birds wintered, 1958–59, in Tralee Bay, Co. Kerry.

Compact flocks of thirty to sixty birds are regularly reported, chiefly at the time of migration.

Knot: *Calidris canutus*

Passage migrant. Winter visitor.

At times of passage, particularly in autumn, the Knot is seen in thousands. Autumn migrants arrive in August, through September, reaching their maximum numbers in October.

Flocks of a thousand or more are found locally in winter, but especially in Strangford Lough and Dublin Bay.

March is the chief month of departure; passage migrants are moving as late as May and June.

There are records for every month but seldom for July.

The smallest numbers are found on the west coast; in Co. Galway it is scarce, in Co. Clare rare. To Co. Wexford it is nowadays a regular visitor, particularly in Wexford Harbour where flocks of from 200 to 500 have been seen between July and September and once in December. Migrants are nowadays regularly reported in Co. Waterford and in winter flocks of up to fifty birds. In Kerry Knots are regular in Tralee Bay, in numbers up to a hundred, and in Dingle Bay, chiefly from September to December and in March and April: about 1,000 have been seen in November.

Parties of five, ten and fifteen are regular inland between August 16th and October 9th; on one occasion a flock of twenty-four was reported.

Knots ringed on migration in Norway in August and September have been found here in winter: an adult ringed in Ireland in July was recovered here in autumn of the following year.

Purple Sandpiper: *Calidris maritima*

Passage migrant. Winter visitor.

The first appear in August, more generally in September and

October. Spring passage is more marked and occurs chiefly in March and April: it extends into May.

On Inishkea off Co. Mayo where passage has been noted from March 21st to April 21st, on three days respectively 175, 140 and 100 were seen; on many other days between ten and seventy-five.

From January to May flocks of up to thirty or fifty are sometimes seen. As a winter visitor the Purple Sandpiper is widespread on rocky coasts, quite exceptionally on sandy shores. It is strangely scarce on the coasts of Cos. Galway and Clare.

There are two June records, one for July.

Little Stint: *Calidris minuta*

Passage migrant in autumn; occasionally in spring.

As an autumn passage migrant the Little Stint is annual, in varying numbers. Occurrences range from July 28th, through August to reach their maximum in September, decrease in October with stragglers in November.

Passage is most marked on the east coast, especially in Belfast Lough, Dublin Bay and on or near the coasts of Co. Wexford. Migrants are seen regularly in western Kerry but in Co. Donegal and on the west coast they are irregular. In Connacht they sometimes come to the seaboard, but more often to inland waters. One has been seen at Lough Funshinagh, Co. Roscommon.

Many records are of single birds but parties of five or six have several times been observed, once twenty-eight, once forty-five and once sixty.

There have been seventeen spring records, ranging between February 13th and May 25th; most in May. There is one June record, three for July. In December 1963 one was seen in Belfast Lough on 14th, two on 20th.

Least Sandpiper: *Calidris minutilla*

Two records.

One was seen on August 24th 1963 at Toome sand-pits on the north-western corner of Lough Neagh, Co. Derry: one at Akeagh Lough, Co. Kerry on August 16th 1965.

Temminck's Stint: *Calidris temminckii*
Ten records.

One was shot near Tralee, Co. Kerry, at the end of January 1848. The following are all sight records of single birds:—One on the River Bann estuary, Co. Derry, on September 11th 1955. One on Rochestown salt-marsh, Co. Kilkenny, on October 12th and 13th 1958. One at Duncrue Street marsh, Belfast, Co. Antrim, on August 28th 1959. One at Lady's Island Lake, Co. Wexford, on September 12th 1959. One at Akeagh Lough, Co. Kerry, on October 7th 1960 and at the same place singly on September 12th 1960, August 16th 1964, September 17th 1964 and August 16th 1965.

Baird's Sandpiper: *Calidris bairdii*
One record.

One was seen at Akeagh Lough, Co. Kerry, where it was present from October 2nd to 6th 1962.

White-rumped Sandpiper: *Calidris fuscicollis*
Vagrant.

There are fourteen records of single birds except when, in one instance, there were two together in Co. Dublin. Occurrences have been on or adjacent to the coast in Kerry (10), Wexford (1), Dublin (1), Antrim (1), Derry (1) and in the months August (1), September (2), October (6), November (1), January (3), February (1).

A specimen in the Ulster Museum, Belfast, is believed to have been killed in Ireland previous to 1836, but there is no certainty about it.

Pectoral Sandpiper: *Calidris melanotos*
Annual vagrant.

Up to 1957 only seven had been recorded. Since 1958 between two and thirteen have been recorded annually. In 1961 alone thirteen birds were seen, in two cases four of them together, in one case three. In 1963 eight were reported singly except in one instance two.

Since 1958 the occurrences have been widespread, but with a bias towards well-watched areas. Kerry (14), Derry (6), Antrim (7), Wexford (4), Dublin (3), Cork, Down, Donegal (2 each), Wicklow, Roscommon (1 each). Inland occurrences were the Derry ones, at Lough Beg and the Roscommon one, at Lough Funchinagh; all others were adjacent to the coast. Autumn occurrences have ranged from August 10th to November 1st: in August (5), September (20), October (11), November (1). April, one from 9th to 13th in 1961; one from May 21st to 26th 1964; one on May 16th 1965; June one from 2nd to 15th in 1963.

Dunlin: *Calidris alpina*

Summer resident. Passage migrant. Winter visitor.

The strongest breeding colony is in Co. Mayo where up to fifty pairs nest. In other localities there are from one to fifteen breeding pairs. A few, probably less than ten pairs in each county, breed very locally in Westmeath, Roscommon, Galway, Sligo, Donegal, Tyrone, Fermanagh, Antrim, Derry, perhaps in Longford.

Dunlin arrive at their breeding haunts at the end of April and in May; they leave again in July.

In Wexford Harbour a flock of 400 in summer plumage was reported on July 4th.

There is passage along the east and west coasts and overland in April, May and June, in October and November.

Outside the breeding season the Dunlin is frequent inland, often in flocks of 1,000 or more birds; such numbers are widespread in suitable haunts in maritime counties.

It is impossible to apportion the numbers of the nominate form *C. a. alpina* and the race *C. a. schinzii* that winter. Specimens of both have been obtained in autumn and winter.

Migrating Dunlin ringed in Norway in September have been found in Co. Antrim and Co. Galway in winter. One migrant ringed in Iceland on July 21st 1964 was found in Co. Wicklow five days later.

Curlew Sandpiper: *Calidris testacea*

Passage migrant in autumn; occasional in spring; rarely in summer and winter.

Passage is usual from August to November. Very few are noticed in spring; there are seven records for March, two for April, seven for May; there are three or four for June, two for July. Most of these records have been for single birds but five were seen together in May.

There are two December reports. On one occasion a bird remained from December 18th to the end of January. There are three records each for January and February.

Migration is most marked on the east coast, in south Co. Wexford and very locally in Co. Kerry. Along the west coast the bird is irregular and scarce; usually seen singly but sometimes two or three together. There are inland records for Cos. Galway and Mayo. Since 1960 one to twelve have been observed regularly at Lough Beg, Co. Derry; there are a number of records for Lough Neagh.

Flocks of less than ten are usual, but twenty to forty together have occasionally been seen.

Numbers fluctuate markedly from year to year.

Western Sandpiper: *Calidris mauri*

Two records.

One was seen beside flood-water near Kilcoole railway station, Co. Wicklow, on October 14th 1960. One was seen at Akeagh Lough where it was present from September 17th to 23rd 1961.

Sanderling: *Crocethia alba*

Passage migrant. Winter visitor.

Adult Sanderlings arrive, occasionally in large numbers, in July, more numerously in early August. They pass on rapidly and are followed in August and September by large flocks in which young birds predominate. Migration is at its height in September and continues into October. Spring migration is noticeable in May, continues on a small scale until the end of June. Some non-breeding birds remain during summer.

Sanderlings are abundant on suitable sandy shores, particularly in Dublin Bay, the coasts of Kerry and Wexford and in Killala Bay, Co. Mayo.

To the northern and north-eastern coasts the bird is a temporary visitor, few remaining in winter. In Lough Foyle and Lough Swilly it is always scarce. On Ballyheigue strand, Co. Kerry, 750 have been seen in December, in Waterford Harbour about 200 on November 26th.

Inland records are for single birds, sometimes parties of six or more seen on Lough Neagh and the large Connacht lakes: twice in August, three times in May, once in June.

Buff-breasted Sandpiper: *Tryngites subruficollis*

Vagrant.

This sandpiper has been recorded eleven times. In two cases two were together, in all others the bird was alone.

Up to 1954 there were only two records concerning three birds. Since then the bird has appeared more frequently. The two early records were of a bird in Co. Dublin and two together in Co. Down, the first previous to 1845, the second in 1864.

Latterly the occurrences have been in Kerry (1), Cork (1), Down (1), Antrim (2), Derry (2), Donegal (2; in one case two birds together). The months—August (2), September (7).

Broad-billed Sandpiper: *Limicola falcinellus*

Two records.

A male shot on October 4th 1844 in Belfast Lough is in the Ulster Museum. One was seen at Duncrue Street marsh, Belfast, Co. Antrim, on May 11th 1963; it remained until the 18th.

Ruff: *Philomachus pugnax*

Passage migrant. Occasional in winter.

In 1954 the Ruff was considered 'uncommon and irregular'. It is now both common and regular as a migrant over most of Ireland. Even in the west Ruffs occur annually; numbers are small but increasing. Favoured places in which Ruffs habitually halt are Lough Beg, Co. Derry; the marshes near Kilcoole, Co. Wicklow, Lady's Island Lake and the Wexford Slobs, Rahasane, Co. Galway and, in Co. Kerry, Akeagh Lough. Carlow, Leix, Louth, Leitrim, Monaghan, Tyrone and Fermanagh are still without a record.

Most occurrences are in coastal areas, but the bird is regular in small numbers at waters far inland. Usually single birds or small parties are observed but flocks of 20 to 30 have been seen and of 48, 75 and about 100 in Co. Wexford.

The Ruff is most numerous in autumn but has occurred in every month. There are seven records for May, eight for June; mostly of single birds. One or two remained at Lough Beg from June 2nd to 16th 1963.

It is increasingly met with in winter. There are about twenty records for December to February concerning some forty birds. Some of these birds may have been wintering. Cases of birds doing so number five and have been in Victoria Park, Belfast (two winters), Akeagh Lough, Co. Kerry (two winters), Co. Wicklow (one winter).

Several males in breeding plumage have been seen.

Avocet: *Recurvirostra avosetta*

Has once bred. Vagrant. Scarce winter visitor.

Two pairs bred successfully at Tacumshin Lake, Co. Wexford, in 1938. In May 1954 two birds came there but did not remain.

As a vagrant the Avocet has been recorded about twenty-five times, usually singly, but sometimes two together and once four. Counties represented in the records are Cork, Waterford, Wexford, Dublin, Antrim, Down, Donegal, Sligo, Mayo (one bird far inland), Galway and in the months, when known, January (3), February (2), May (2), July (2), August (1), December (2). In addition, two birds on the North Slob, Co. Wexford, on January 6th 1956 were joined by two more on February 1st; all had left by February 25th.

In Cork Harbour two wintered in 1956–57, six in 1957–58, two in 1958–59 and 1959–60, three in 1960–61, five in 1961–62, seven, initially eight, in 1962–63. None wintered in 1963–64 though a single bird was present in February 1964 and January 1965. One seen at Shanagarry on December 1st 1964 was perhaps the same bird as one in the Cork Harbour haunt at the end of December 1964.

Black-winged Stilt: *Himantopus himantopus*
Nine records.

One was seen near Youghal, Co. Cork, in the winter of 1823 or 1824. One was shot near Ballinrobe, Co. Mayo, in January 1836(?). One was obtained at Clontarf, Co. Dublin, previous to 1837. Three were seen together at Adare, Co. Limerick, previous to 1841. A flock from which one was shot was seen on Castlemaine Bay, Co. Kerry, previous to 1850. Of two seen, one was shot, near Kilbeggan, Co. Westmeath, many years previous to 1890. One was shot on Tory Island, Co. Donegal, in April 1916. One frequented a marsh near Clonakilty, Co. Cork, from mid-April to early June 1942. One was seen on the estuary of the Arragideen River, near Timoleague, Co. Cork, on September 11th 1949; on October 3rd another accompanied it.

Grey Phalarope: *Phalaropus fulicarius*
Passage migrant.

The Grey Phalarope occurs almost annually as a passage migrant in autumn and early winter, chiefly along the west coast, more irregularly on the east coast. Occasionally it is found inland as a storm-driven waif. Single occurrences in March, April and June are on record.

There is a noticeable movement of phalaropes, the majority being of this species, off Cape Clear, Co. Cork, from the end of August to October. Between September 14th and 22nd 1960 it was phenomenal. Over 120 phalaropes were recorded on 17th, over 380 on 20th. Both Grey and Red-necked Phalaropes were involved, but their relative proportion was impossible to assess; certainly most were probably Grey Phalaropes. A widespread passage at this period was noticed elsewhere on our coasts.

Red-necked Phalarope: *Phalaropus lobatus*
Summer visitor to one locality. Scarce passage migrant.

Following the discovery in 1902 of a colony in Co. Mayo, two subsidiary sites of two or three and six pairs respectively were found, but breeding in them had ceased by 1944.

In Donegal single pairs bred on Roaninish and near Murroe for several years about 1925.

In 1905 about fifty pairs were breeding in the main Mayo colony. Numbers declined from 1929 (about forty pairs). Now only one to three pairs breed.

Birds usually arrive at the nesting place in early May, have nests by mid-June and depart in August.

In each of the years 1954 to 1961 and in 1963 a few have been recorded on autumn passage in July (2), August (2), September (11), November (2), December (1). Most cases were of single birds; on one September day six were together. In addition there were undoubtedly some numbers off Cape Clear in September 1960 (see under Grey Phalarope).

In June there are seven records at a period when the breeding stock had already arrived.

Coastal occurrences have been well scattered. There are only three reports for inland waters when single birds were seen, in each case at the end of June, on Lough Ennell, Co. Westmeath, Levally Lough near Tuam, Co. Galway, and on Lough Neagh.

Wilson's Phalarope: *Phalaropus tricolor*

One record.

One in almost winter plumage was seen at Lady's Island Lake, Co. Wexford, on August 12th and 13th 1961.

Stone Curlew: *Burhinus oedicnemus*

Vagrant.

There are sixteen records of single birds obtained or seen at long intervals and in the months October to May inclusive. Of the occurrences six have taken place since 1900.

Distribution by counties: Dublin (6), Wexford (2), Clare, Cork, Waterford, Kilkenny, Galway, Donegal, Antrim (one each). For one of the records the county is unknown.

Pratincole: *Glareola pratincola*

Two or three records.

One that was shot at Castlefreke, Co. Cork, in October previous to 1844 was fully described and the identification accepted at the time. Some doubt must, however, exist about this record.

One was seen on August 23rd 1953 at Crusheen, Co. Clare. A bird of the Black-winged form *Glareola nordmanni*, shot near Belmullet, Co. Mayo, on August 23rd 1935, was an immature female. It is in the Ulster Museum, Belfast.

Cream-coloured Courser: *Cursorius cursor*

One record.

One was seen in the sandhills near Raven Point, Wexford Harbour, in either the last week of December 1952 or the first week of January 1953.

Great Skua: *Catharacta skua*

Passage migrant.

Previous to 1950 only about thirty occurrences were known. Since then, partly due, no doubt, to intensive 'sea-watching', the Great Skua is nowadays known as a regular passage migrant in considerable numbers.

Passage northward along the west coast is from mid-March to the end of April; southward migration is in August, September and early October. One was seen between Skelligs and Tearaght off Co. Kerry on December 3rd 1964.

Although there are a number of records for Co. Wexford, the movement through the Irish Sea is small and could not account for the heavy movement observed at Cape Clear, Co. Cork, past which considerable numbers fly westward both in spring and autumn. A minimum of 134 passed Cape Clear in autumn 1962, 493 in 1963. A total of 237 was seen off Erris Head, Co. Mayo, between mid-August and mid-September 1961. Forty passed Cape Clear on April 14th 1963 and off Inishkea fifty-one passed between mid-March and mid-April 1961. Numbers are less spectacular off Tory Island and Malin Head, Co. Donegal, though at the latter forty-seven have been seen between September 17th and October 4th. A passage of small numbers is noticed at St. John's Point, Co. Down.

In spite of the large totals the mean number passing Cape Clear was only three birds per hour at the peak period of passage.

Migration is regular along the south coast, but reaches its greatest intensity off Cape Clear.

Seventeen together were observed around a fishing boat three miles south of Cork Harbour on September 28th 1964.

Inland one was found dead near Thurles, Co. Tipperary, in November 1894; one was shot on Lough Derg in October 1959; one that had been ringed as a chick in Iceland in July was caught in a fishing net in Lough Corrib on September 23rd 1963.

Arctic Skua: *Stercorarius parasiticus*

Passage migrant.

Until quite recently the Arctic was considered the most numerous skua visiting Ireland. Nowadays the numbers are far exceeded by those of the Great Skua. There have been autumns when exceptional numbers have been recorded; such was the case in October 1851.

There is a clear pattern in autumn of southward migration down the west coast with rather greater numbers, in some years, traversing the Irish Sea. Inland passage is fairly regular in autumn; such as has been noted on the Connacht lakes, in the Shannon valley and here and there elsewhere. Birds are fewer in spring on the coasts and are irregular inland. Passage is normal between April 1st and May 17th but occasionally extends into June. On June 19th 1963 twenty-five flew west at Cape Clear. There are about eight July records, mostly on the west coast, in the second half of the month.

One was seen in Co. Down on December 5th 1954, another in Tralee Bay, Co. Kerry, on December 11th 1963.

Pomarine Skua: *Stercorarius pomarinus*

Passage migrant.

This skua is a regular passage migrant in small numbers and on all coasts both in spring and autumn. There are inland records in Tipperary (1), Westmeath (2), Kildare (2), Roscommon (1) and several on the large lakes in Co. Mayo. Records by months: April (3; earliest 22nd), May (12), June (2), July (3), August (16), September (30), October (19), November (10), December (5).

Most records are of single birds or two or three together. There were ten together off Cape Clear in April; four together off St. John's Point, Co. Down, and seven together off Co. Wexford in May, all in different years.

Pale phase birds preponderate in the records and where the phase has been noted forty-two have been pale, about twelve dark.

Note. At Cape Clear, Co. Cork, in 1963, of skuas fully identified 75% were Great, 21% Arctic, 4% Pomarine. For the previous four years comparable figures were 84%, 14% and 2% respectively.

Long-tailed Skua: *Stercorarius longicaudus*

Scarce irregular passage migrant.

There are about fifty records of this skua. Most have been reported on the coasts of Connacht (13) and Ulster (19); in Munster (7), Leinster (10). Ten of the occurrences were in inland localities, widely scattered.

Occurrences have been very irregular and mostly in May (5) and June (5), September (7) and October (13). There are records for March (1), April (1), August (4) and November (1; when 4 were seen in Co. Donegal).

Since 1954 only three have been reported: an immature bird found dead near Mullingar, Co. Westmeath, on October 6th 1955; an adult seen in Ballyheigue Bay, Co. Kerry, on September 24th 1958 and an immature bird found dying on the Co. Cork coast on August 22nd 1960.

An account is given (*Birds of Ireland* (1900)) of large flocks of skuas seen on the River Shannon in May 1860 from which three were shot and believed to have been of this species. The specimens have never been traced and it seems very improbable that they were examined by any competent ornithologist.

The two specimens in the National Museum show affinities closer to the typical form rather than to the Iceland race, *pallescens*.

Ivory Gull: *Pagophila eburnea*

Six records.

Two together, of which one was shot, at Blennerville, Co. Kerry, in February 1847. One was shot in Bantry Bay, Co. Cork, on January 31st 1852. One was found dead at Belmullet, Co. Mayo, on March 27th 1905. One was picked up dead on the Marina,

Cork, on February 16th 1913. One was shot at Teelin Pier, Co. Donegal, on March 13th 1913. One was seen at Donaghadee, Co. Down, on various dates from March 1st to April 3rd 1931. The Mayo and Donegal specimens are in the National Museum.

Great Black-backed Gull: *Larus marinus*

Resident. Partial migrant. Winter visitor.

This gull has greatly increased in numbers in recent years. It breeds on many marine islands and on the mainland coast. There are numerous colonies of up to between fifteen and twenty pairs. The strength of few colonies and of none of the more inaccessible ones has been checked since about 1950. The following are the largest known: In Strangford Lough, Co. Down, 49 pairs on South Minnis Island in 1956 and about 40 pairs on Drummond Island. In Co. Wexford, Great Saltee had 89 pairs in 1950, about 150 in 1964; Little Saltee about 200 pairs in 1963; Keeragh Islands 90 pairs in 1961. On High Island, Co. Galway, there were about 50 pairs in 1943. On Bills Rocks, Co. Mayo, about 50 pairs in 1932.

A few pairs nest on large inland lakes in Mayo and Galway and on small ones in Donegal. In 1961 a pair bred on Lough Ree, Co. Longford.

After breeding there is dispersal. A young bird ringed on the Kerry coast in 1953 and another in 1955 were recovered in winter in Portugal and France in 1954 and 1956 respectively.

About five nestlings ringed in Iceland have been found in Ireland in winter.

This gull is found far inland in all months, most numerously in winter and in March, least often in August: sometimes ten or fifteen, occasionally thirty or more are together.

It is more abundant on the east coast than on the west in winter. In favoured areas flocks of up to 100 birds are seen, but otherwise flocks of about thirty are more usual.

Lesser Black-backed Gull: *Larus fuscus*

Larus fuscus graellsii: Summer visitor. Passage migrant. A few winter.

This race breeds extensively, chiefly on marine islands, but on some large inland lakes. Recently it has greatly increased.

No recent check has been made at the majority of breeding stations listed in *Birds of Ireland* (1954). Present knowledge is of breeding in Co. Kerry; two stations, one of them containing 25 pairs. Co. Cork, scattered pairs. At Cape Clear 36 pairs in 1963. Co. Clare, isolated pairs breed on islands in Lough Derg and a pair nested at Ballyeighter Lough in 1961. Co. Wexford, Great Saltee, over 30 nests in 1953, 67 in 1955, 120 in 1960 and 350 in 1964; Little Saltee, over 200 breeding pairs in 1963, eleven pairs on the Keeragh Islands, 1961. Co. Dublin, two or three stations; one at Lambay has recently increased from 20 to 80 pairs. Co. Longford, near Goat's Island, Lough Ree, ten pairs in 1948 had increased to fifty in 1961. Co. Galway, islands in Lough Corrib; High Island is the only maritime station. Co. Mayo, breeding stations of from one to ten pairs on four marine islands, on a fifth there were 25 pairs in 1944. On Lough Mask the largest inland colony contains over 50 pairs and there are several smaller ones and two of less than 30 pairs on Lough Conn. Co. Sligo, one or two pairs were breeding on Bomore Rock in 1948. Co. Leitrim, it breeds on two islands on Lough Allen. Co. Fermanagh, a few pairs on Lower Lough Erne. Co. Down, about 50 pairs breed on John's Island, smaller numbers on Mew Island, about 40 pairs in Strangford Lough. Co. Antrim, a few breed on Muck Island and on the mainland coast, about 40 pairs on Rathlin Island. It no longer breeds on the Star Bog. Co. Armagh, under 20 pairs on Coney and Crogan Islands, Lough Neagh, for the first time in 1964. Co. Donegal, a few breed on Aranmore and Inishtrahull; in 1947 a few were doing so on Roaninish.

Arrivals take place from mid-February, in greater numbers in March and April, those in April perhaps being passage migrants. Birds are at their breeding stations in March, often early in that month.

After breeding the birds move away rapidly from their breeding areas.

Autumn migration occurs from August to mid-October with stragglers to the end of November; it is most noticeable in September. Migration on the west coast is little noticed and in Connacht both in spring and autumn is chiefly of birds moving overland.

Here and there birds, chiefly singly, are seen in winter; there is no evidence of any tendency towards an increase of numbers in winter.

The Scandinavian form (*Larus f. fuscus*) has been recorded twenty-six times. Nowadays one or two are reported almost annually, and in the months August to October, December, January, March to May; the majority in September and March. There are two instances in which respectively four and nine were together.

Herring Gull: *Larus argentatus*

Resident.

In recent years there has been a very marked increase in the numbers breeding and the bird is extending its breeding range. There are colonies on many marine islands, mainland cliffs and nowadays on some bogs and several freshwater lakes far inland.

The only large colonies of which there is accurate numerical record are those of Great Saltee; there were about 2,000 pairs in 1960, about 3,500 pairs in 1964. These numbers probably are comparable to many of the larger colonies on our coasts.

Non-breeding birds are widespread far inland in summer. In winter ever increasingly large flocks have been noticed since about 1935 where at bacon factories in the interior of the country 1,000 and more assemble.

The only form of migration would seem to be of dispersal.

A Herring Gull with the characteristics of the Yellow-legged race *Larus a. michahellis*, was seen at Rosscarbery, Co. Cork, on October 12th 1955. Weather charts indicated conditions more favourable to the appearance on the southern coast of Ireland of this Mediterranean race rather than the northern form *Larus a. omissus*.

Common Gull: *Larus canus*

Resident. Passage migrant. Winter visitor.

The Common Gull breeds commonly on the lakes of Donegal and on a few islands off that coast. A few pairs nest in Co. Sligo. In Co. Mayo more breed than in any other county, in colonies large and small. The largest colony in Ireland is that on Lough Carrowmore (about 200 pairs); Loughs Conn, Carra and Mask have a large total population. It breeds on several marine islands off the Mullet. In Co. Galway the Common Gull is less widespread than in Mayo and the colonies seldom exceed twenty pairs. None breeds in Galway or Mayo east of the large Connacht lakes nor in Connacht south of Galway Bay.

One or two pairs have bred in Co. Roscommon. In 1963 six pairs had nests on Goat's Island, Lough Ree, Co. Longford, in 1964 eleven.

In Co. Kerry about twenty pairs breed on the Magharee Islands; in 1955 it was breeding on Illaunboy and Beginish off Dunquin. Small numbers breed in Co. Down, Fermanagh, Antrim and Derry.

In Connacht Common Gulls arrive at their inland breeding stations in mid-February, at coastal stations about ten days later. Colonies are vacated during the second half of July; dispersal is rapid and flocks are found in August on all coasts.

During autumn and winter few first-year birds are seen.

Some Common Gulls disperse beyond our shores, two having been recovered, one in Scotland, the other in Cornwall. The only evidence of emigration of our breeding birds to the Continent lies in a nestling ringed in Co. Kerry in 1955 being found in Spain in September 1957.

Heavy passage movement occurs in spring and autumn. In winter this gull is widespread on suitable coasts; in maritime counties of the west it is common inland. In central Ireland it is seldom seen, though in one locality in Co. Roscommon considerable numbers are present each winter.

Before 1955 it was considered rare on the coast of Co. Cork, but since then has been increasingly noted and is now regular in winter. Flocks of about 120, 200 and 300 were reported in different places in November and December 1964.

Young ringed in Germany, Denmark, Norway, Sweden and Estonia have been recovered here in winter.

Glaucous Gull: *Larus hyperboreus*

Scarce winter visitor. Occurrences in every month.

The Glaucous Gull is reported annually, usually singly, but sometimes two to five together. The total annual occurrences average about five over the past ten years and involve about sixty birds.

Occurrences take place most frequently in December, January and February, not often in May, June or August and only rarely in every other month.

Occasionally individuals make a protracted stay, thus one remained in Dingle Harbour, Co. Kerry, from March 1st 1963 until May 3rd 1964. On arrival it was sub-adult and the very gradual change to adult plumage was noticeable. An adult stayed in Dingle Harbour from March 3rd to May 28th; a first-winter bird from February 28th to March 23rd. A second-winter bird was at Blennerville, Co. Kerry, from July 21st to September 15th.

Glaucous Gulls are recorded on all coasts, seldom on the east coast, most frequently from those of the north, north-east and west, very regularly in Kerry. At a time when, over several years, an area at Limerick City was regularly watched, one or more were seen annually.

There have been inland occurrences in Cos. Antrim and Dublin and at the bacon factories as far inland as Castlebar and Claremorris in Co. Mayo.

Most have been in immature plumage. There are seven records of birds in the unusual white second-winter plumage.

Iceland Gull: *Larus glaucoides*

Scarce but regular winter visitor. Occurrences in most months.

Up to about 1950 the Iceland Gull was recorded rather irregularly, but since 1954 occurrences have been annual. Three to six are usually seen each year, in 1958 and 1960 seven were reported. All reports have been of single birds.

Occurrences take place on all coasts but rarely on that of the south. North-east Ulster, Co. Dublin, west Kerry, Connacht and Donegal provide the majority of records.

Previous to 1950 the Iceland Gull was considered to occur most often in December, January and February; there were records for every month. Since 1954 we have the following picture: January, 11; February, 4; March, 4; April, 10; May, 4; June, 2; July, 3; September, 1; October, 1; November, 6; and December, 4.

A gull showing the marked characteristics of an adult Kumlien's Gull (*Larus g. kumlieni*) was seen on January 10th 1958 at Tralee, Co. Kerry.

Mediterranean Black-headed Gull: *Larus melanocephalus*
Three records.

One was seen in Belfast Lough on September 1st 1956. An adult was seen off the Copeland Islands, Co. Down, on September 6th 1958. One was seen on a beach near the Old Head of Kinsale, Co. Cork, on October 4th 1964.

Bonaparte's Gull: *Larus philadelphia*
One record.

A male in winter plumage shot on February 1st 1848 on the River Lagan, near Belfast, is in the Ulster Museum, Belfast.

Little Gull: *Larus minutus.*
Vagrant; recorded in every month.

Up to 1952 a total of twenty-four had been recorded in the months August to February and in May. Since 1954 occurrences have been annual. Numbers reported have varied. Years having five or more reports were 1956 (5), 1958 (18), 1959 (6), 1962 (8; in one case two birds), 1963 (8), 1965 (13; in two cases two birds together). In 1961 in one case three birds were together.

Since 1954 the months of occurrence have been January (2), February (2), March (5), April (5), May (12), June (3), July (4), August (7), September (17), October (5), November (4). Thus it will be seen that September and May are the chief months of occurrence.

Records are for all the coastal counties except Waterford, Clare, Leitrim, Louth. Some of the birds were seen at inland waters, once far up the River Shannon, in central Ireland.

Of the records, where age has been recorded, the proportion of immature birds has been just double that of adults.

Although the increase in numbers is perhaps partly due to increased watching, there can be little doubt that it is also real.

Black-headed Gull: *Larus ridibundus*
Resident. Partial migrant. Winter visitor.

This gull is abundant at all seasons. It breeds in great numbers on some bogs, in considerable numbers in marshes, on islands in freshwater lakes and in small numbers on marine islands off Donegal, Down and Antrim.

As a breeding bird it is scarce near the east coast, No breeding place is known in Louth, nor in Waterford. For two years, about 1916, some 80 pairs bred at Akeagh Lough, Co. Kerry, but vacated the site on the lowering of the water-level.

Breeding grounds are reached early in March and vacated about mid-August.

Many non-breeding birds frequent the coasts in summer and these are later joined by the breeding stock.

This gull becomes less plentiful inland in autumn but numbers increase noticeably in mid-January.

First-year birds which are not much in evidence in winter increase markedly in early February and March on both the east and west coasts.

A large proportion at least of birds of the year emigrate to the Continent and birds from England and the Continent come here to winter. One ringed in Iceland was recovered in winter.

Sabine's Gull: *Xema sabini*

Vagrant.

Of the thirty-four records of this gull only eight were of adult birds.

Occurrences have taken place in Cork (4), Limerick (1), Galway (1), Dublin (9), Wicklow (2), Down (5), Antrim (4), Down or Antrim (2), Derry (2), Donegal (2), Westmeath (1), Lough Derg (1).

The months have been August to December with a large majority in September; one in April.

Except once when two were seen together, all records have been of single birds.

Kittiwake: *Rissa tridactyla*

Summer visitor. Scarce in winter. Perhaps passage migrant.

There are dense colonies on precipitous coasts and islands of all maritime counties except Louth, Meath, Leitrim and Down where suitable cliffs are lacking.

Nearly all stations where breeding has taken place in more than one year since 1900 are shown on a map, figure 1, in *Bird Study*, 10: p. 148.

Nests have been counted at few colonies but some figures are available: Rathlin Island, 983 in 1958; Lambay, about 450 in 1959; Ireland's Eye, 160 in 1959; Great Saltee, 1,214 in 1959, about 2,000 in 1960, about 3,000 in 1964. Dunmore East, 877 in 1959; development in the area has upset this colony though it seems likely that the birds will re-establish themselves in the vicinity: there were between 450 and 600 nests in 1965. Bull Rock, 200 in 1955 but none on Cow Rock. Great Skellig, about 448 in 1958, 400 to 450 in 1964. Inishtearaght, 155 in 1955. Blackrock (Mayo) about 500 in 1943. Cliffs near the stack Moistha, Co. Mayo, 100 to 150 in 1959. Tormore Island, Co. Donegal, 150–200 pairs in 1964. There are many stations with ten to fifty nests.

Kittiwakes return to their breeding stations in March. A noticeable northward movement on the west coast occurs in March and April.

Breeding haunts are deserted in August. Birds remain inshore until October, after which few are seen.

On the west coast a south-westerly movement takes place in autumn. On the north-east coast Kittiwakes pass in spring and autumn.

There are a few records of the sudden appearance of numbers in winter. Many were in Cork Harbour for about a fortnight in January 1948. About 500 were off Co. Down on December 16th 1956.

There are records of birds seen inland irregularly on Lough Neagh, Lower Lough Erne and once at Enniskillen in winter. Ten were seen on Lough Neagh in February 1959. In September an immature bird was seen in Co. Clare over thirty miles inland.

Black Tern: *Chlidonias niger*

Passage migrant.

The Black Tern is nowadays an annual passage migrant in varying numbers, both in spring and autumn. Formerly it was considered a rare vagrant.

This tern has been recorded in all the provinces and in every month except January, February and March. Most appear in May, September and early October. There is a record of one bird on October 31st, of one on November 15th, and one in December.

The Black Tern is often seen singly, but small parties occur. Flocks of sixteen and twenty-one have been seen on Lough Carra, Co. Mayo, in September. More than thirty-five were scattered over Dublin Bay on May 5th 1960. There were thirty-three in Belfast Lough on August 30th 1960.

It often appears far inland. Passage is noticed but not annually, in the Shannon valley and along the large Connacht lakes.

Occurrences in May 1959 were particularly numerous. The autumns of 1958 and 1960 were notable for the numbers seen.

White-winged Black Tern: *Chlidonias leucopterus*
Vagrant.

There are eleven records of single birds in the counties Cork (1; 1936), Kerry (1; 1963), Clare (1; 1893), Limerick (1; 1875), Tipperary (2; 1874, 1943), Lough Derg (1; 1962), Waterford (1; 1875), Dublin (2; 1841, undated), Donegal (1; 1964), and in the months May (3), June (3), July (2), October (2).

Whiskered Tern: *Chlidonias hybrida*
Two records.

An adult shot at the mouth of the River Liffey, Co. Dublin, in September 1839 is in the National Museum. One was seen at Buckroney marsh, Co. Wicklow, on June 19th 1961.

Gull-billed Tern: *Gelochelidon nilotica*
One record.

An adult was seen on August 16th 1957 over the Herdman channel, Belfast, Co. Antrim.

Caspian Tern: *Hydroprogne caspia*
One record.

One was seen off Tory Island, Co. Donegal, on October 10th 1959.

Royal Tern: *Sterna maxima*

One record.

One was picked up dead on the North Bull, Co. Dublin, on March 24th 1954. Exhaustive research excluded any suggestion that the bird had drifted to Co. Dublin as a corpse and showed that there was every reason to treat the case as one of a genuine vagrant.

Common Tern: *Sterna hirundo*

Summer visitor. Probable passage migrant.

The Common Tern breeds in colonies varying in strength from a few pairs to those few which contain over 1,000 pairs. There are many colonies of about fifty pairs, but numbers in all colonies rise and fall erratically. Sites too are often changed. Nowadays it breeds chiefly on marine islands or near the mainland coasts. The once flourishing colonies on inland lakes have decreased to negligible proportions or have disappeared.

No very recent assessment of colonies is available. In Co. Cork considerable numbers breed in Bantry Bay. In Co. Kerry about 70 pairs breed on Illaunturlough in Tralee Bay; in 1957 about 60 pairs became established on Lough Currane. There are now only two colonies in Co. Wexford, one of which contained 1,500 pairs in 1963. In Co. Dublin one colony only is now known. In Co. Down the colonies on the Copeland Islands and in Carlingford Lough total in each case 50–100 pairs, smaller numbers nest in Strangford Lough. The only regular colony in Co. Antrim is on the Maidens. The largest of a number of colonies in Co. Galway is that of about 500 pairs on Mutton Island in Galway Bay. In Co. Mayo the strongest colonies are on the Mullet and in Killala Bay, but in no case does their strength exceed 50 pairs. Up to 100 pairs breed on Inishmurray, Co. Sligo. In western Co. Donegal there are a number of colonies of under 50 pairs. In 1957 this tern bred for the first time at Lough Beg, Co. Derry; the average is ten breeding pairs though in 1958 there were twenty-one. In Co. Westmeath about twenty pairs were breeding on Lough Derryvaragh in 1965.

The Common Tern arrives early in May and departs in September. It has been seen on April 12th; there are several reports of it during the last week of April; stragglers occur in October; there is a record of one on November 15th and of one, recently dead, on December 27th.

Arctic Tern: *Sterna macrura*

Summer visitor. Probable passage migrant.

The numbers breeding have decreased greatly during the present century. With the exception of Lower Lough Erne, all inland haunts have been deserted.

On Roancarrigmore, Co. Cork, up to 100 pairs nest; in Co. Kerry about 10 pairs in Tralee Bay. Co. Wexford's only colony consists of 50 to 100 pairs; the three former sites have been abandoned. A few islands off the coasts of Cos. Galway and Mayo have colonies of less than 10 pairs, though off the Mullet one colony contains about 50 pairs. The largest in these two counties is one of about 100 pairs in Killala Bay. The largest Irish colony is on Inishmurray, Co. Sligo, where 400 to 450 pairs nest. About 30 pairs breed on islands at the entrance to Sligo Bay. On the Copeland Islands, Co. Down, less than 50 pairs breed; about 30 to 50 pairs do so in Strangford and Carlingford Loughs. There is a colony on Maidens, Co. Antrim.

Arctic Terns breed on some of the lakes adjacent to the coast in west Co. Donegal and on islands off that coast, the strongest colony being of about 20 pairs.

Like other species of tern, it is unstable and colonies fluctuate in size and sites are frequently changed.

Arctic Terns arrive in May; they depart in September or October, in both of which months there is what appears to be passage migration.

Roseate Tern: *Sterna dougallii*

Summer visitor.

The largest known colony, about 2,000 pairs, was in Co. Wexford in 1962. Numbers there had dropped considerably by 1964. There were 68 pairs at Rockabill, Co. Dublin, in 1958 but the number has decreased to about 30 pairs. In Co. Down there are five colonies; on the Copeland Islands, on Burial Island and in Strangford and Carlingford Loughs. In the last the colony varies in strength up to thirty-eight pairs.

As an illustration of the state of fluctuation, the numbers breeding at one of the above colonies during the past six years have been 150, 363, 400, 50, 30 and 6.

Single pairs, rarely two or three, have been found nesting in colonies of other terns off the coasts of Donegal, Sligo, Galway and Cork. In Co. Clare about ten pairs were found near Ballyvaughan in 1961, but storms washed away the habitat before 1962. In 1952 a pair was suspected of breeding in Tralee Bay, Co. Kerry.

Roseate Terns arrive during the second half of May; one was obtained in March 1841, off Co. Antrim. Departure is in early September; there are October records, one being for 18th.

Bridled Tern: *Sterna anaethetus*

One record.

On November 29th 1953 an adult in winter plumage was picked up freshly dead on the shore of the North Bull, Co. Dublin.

The specimen was submitted to critical examination and found referable to the race *Sterna a. melanoptera.* It is in the National Museum.

Little Tern: *Sterna albifrons*

Summer visitor.

There are many scattered and small colonies of this tern, chiefly on the east and west coasts. In Co. Cork about 15 pairs bred from 1934 to 1936; in 1962 in a locality where four pairs nested, sixteen or seventeen did so in 1964. These are the only known instances of breeding in Munster.

In Co. Wexford there was a colony of 75 to 100 pairs in 1963; in Co. Wicklow on a short stretch of coast 25 to 30 pairs breed. Colonies of more than twenty-five pairs are exceptional.

Sporadic breeding occurs in Louth, Galway, Mayo, Sligo and Donegal. A colony of about 20 pairs on Tory Island, Co. Donegal, is of very recent origin. From time to time breeding takes place at one locality on the coast of Co. Derry.

Inland records are exceptional but have been reported on Lough Corrib in June, on Lough Beg, Co. Derry, in July and on Lough Carra, Co. Mayo, on September 13th when five were together.

The Little Tern has been seen on April 14th and 26th; most arrive during the first half of May.

Heavy movement has been reported along the Co. Wexford coast between July 22nd and August 3rd: on August 1st nearly 200 birds passed in an unspecified, but not long, period.

Normally departure is in September with stragglers up to October 31st.

Sandwich Tern: *Sterna sandvicensis*

Summer visitor. Possibly passage migrant.

Since this tern was first found breeding in Ireland in 1850, many colonies have been established on marine islands, more generally on freshwater lakes, especially in the west.

The Sandwich Tern is even more capricious in respect of its breeding places than others of its genus. Sites are constantly changed and numbers fluctuate greatly.

It has been breeding in Co. Wexford since about 1934; there was a colony of about 150 pairs in 1963. In Co. Galway there is one fairly regularly used site; a few breed elsewhere spasmodically. Co. Mayo has had a maximum of six sites in occupation at one time. At Cross Lough (Louisburgh) a colony of about seventy-five pairs is the largest. A few pairs breed in Co. Sligo. There is one strong colony in Co. Donegal. In Co. Down small colonies flourish in Strangford Lough and about 100 pairs in Carlingford Lough; breeding takes place spasmodically and in varying numbers on Mew Island and Burial Island. In Co. Kerry a pair bred in Tralee Bay in 1955 and since then up to ten pairs have done so in the same group of islands. In 1965 a pair attemped to breed on the Co. Wicklow coast.

The Sandwich Tern is frequently reported in March, sometimes as early as 15th. There is one record for March 2nd in Co. Down. Most arrive in early April. Breeding grounds are abandoned at the end of July or early in August. Birds dally on the coasts throughout September. Southward movement is noticed in October.

Evidence of inland migration via the Connacht lakes and the Shannon valley is very meagre and then in spring.

What appeared to be a large-scale northward passage movement was once witnessed along the Co. Dublin coast on June 2nd.

Razorbill: *Alca torda*

Summer visitor. Scarce in winter.

The Razorbill breeds in large colonies wherever there are suitable marine cliffs. Its notable breeding stations are the Cliffs of Moher and cliffs near Kilkee, Co. Clare; the Skelligs and Tearaght off Co. Kerry; the Bull Rock, Co. Cork; Inishmore and Inishark off Co. Galway; Clare Island, Bills Rocks, Blackrock and the cliffs of north Mayo; Aughris Head, Co. Sligo; Tormore, Malin Head and Horn Head, Co. Donegal, and Rathlin Island, Co. Antrim. On the east coast it breeds on Lambay, Ireland's Eye and a few on Wicklow Head; in Co. Wexford on Great Saltee, but only in small numbers on the coast of Waterford.

Only at Great Saltee has an accurate count of breeding numbers been made: about 10,000 in 1960, the same number in 1964.

In March great numbers appear in the vicinity of the coasts. Razorbills come on to the cliffs early in March, sometimes at the end of February; in the north it is early April before they land.

Breeding haunts are vacated at the end of July. From August to November the Razorbill is numerous off the coasts. In November and December great numbers have been seen passing southward, but normally few Razorbills are seen in December or other winter months.

A young bird ringed on the Bull Rock, Co. Cork, in July was recovered in the following December in Spain.

Storm-driven individuals have been reported in most inland counties.

Great Auk: *Alca impennis*

Extinct.

This bird is considered to have been abundant in former times.

Little Auk: *Plautus alle*

Irregular winter visitor. Probably annual in autumn.

Reports of the Little Auk are generally in the months November to February as the result of storms causing 'wrecks'. At such times storm-driven victims have been found widespread on and near coasts and far inland. Reports have come from every county except Longford, Roscommon, Cavan and Monaghan.

The last disastrous 'wreck' took place in mid-February 1950.

Some are driven ashore almost every winter on the Mullet, Co. Mayo.

With increased 'sea-watching', evidence of movement along the west coast is accumulating. Individuals are seen almost annually between August 15th and October 8th. Two were seen passing Great Saltee, Co. Wexford, on September 7th.

There is a record of one in March off Co. Waterford; one in summer plumage in Tralee Bay, Co. Kerry, on April 14th. During a six-hour watch on April 3rd two single birds were seen to pass Malin Head, Co. Donegal and off Cape Clear, Co. Cork, one was seen on April 20th. On May 22nd 1846 one was obtained in Ulster. June and July are the only months without record.

Guillemot: *Uria aalge*

Resident. Winter visitor.

The Southern Guillemot (*Uria a. albionis*) breeds in large colonies on cliffs and marine islands. The most notable breeding stations are those on the Skelligs and Tearaght, Co. Kerry; the Bull and Cow Rocks off Co. Cork; the Cliffs of Moher in Clare; Inishark, Inishmore, Co. Galway; Clare Island, Inishturk, Blackrock, Bills Rocks and the cliffs of north Mayo; Aughris Head is the only station in Co. Sligo; Tormore, Malin Head and Horn Head in Co. Donegal and Rathlin Island, Co. Antrim; Great Saltee, Co. Wexford. There are many colonies of lesser strength. On the east coast Lambay, Howth Head and Ireland's Eye are the only stations.

During the past twenty years numbers are thought to have declined. At Great Saltee there was a decrease, but since 1960 the population has remained at about 15,000 breeding pairs. The estimated number breeding on Doonmore stack, Rathlin Island, is 10,000. In 1939 about 1,000 pairs were breeding on Aughris Head, in 1949 about 800. Full counts have not been made elsewhere.

Guillemots arrive in thousands on the cliffs of Great Saltee in November, spending several hours on the ledges. It is late March when they land on their northern breeding sites.

By the first week in August Guillemots have deserted the cliffs.

Many are seen off the south and east coasts in winter, but off the Connacht coast the Guillemot is rarely seen in early winter.

The variety known as the 'Bridled' or 'Ringed' Guillemot is found on all the coasts. In colonies on the south and east coasts the proportion of this form is about 2%; on the north and west coasts 5% to 6%.

The Northern Guillemot (*Uria a. aalge*) is a winter visitor off all coasts. Birds showing the characters of this form have been identified in the months September to February. Specimens have been obtained off the coasts of Dublin, Mayo, Cork and Kerry, in which county one was also obtained inland; one was captured on the Antrim coast.

Brunnich's Guillemot: *Uria lomvia*

Two records.

One was seen off Kilcoole, Co. Wicklow, on September 24th 1938, another off Dun Laoghaire, Co. Dublin, on October 25th 1945. Less satisfactorily identified was a probable off Dun Laoghaire on December 31st 1955.

Black Guillemot: *Uria grylle*

Resident.

The Black Guillemot breeds locally on coasts and low marine islands with suitably rocky shores and especially in south-west Cork, Kerry, Galway, Mayo and Donegal. Recently numbers have increased in Donegal and on the east coast, especially at Bray Head, Co. Wicklow, where in the breeding season a loose flock of fifty or more birds has been seen. On the coasts of Co. Louth and Co. Down there are breeding places in derelict quays and in the walls of harbours and piers. Recently the bird has bred at Kilkeel and northward in Co. Down. In Derry it breeds only at Castlerock. Elsewhere on the north coast it breeds fairly commonly. Very few breed on the Waterford and Wexford coasts.

Though not given to flocking, twenty-six have been seen together in April; loose flocks of up to 100 birds have been reported and once one of over 200 on the Connemara coast on September 27th.

Photo: Ian Finlay

(A) DERREENS ISLAND, LOUGH CARROWMORE, CO. MAYO. INLAND BREEDING SITE OF MANY COMMON GULLS AND SANDWICH TERNS

Photo: David Cabot

(B) SAND DUNES, CO. WEXFORD. BREEDING PLACE OF THE LARGEST COLONY OF ROSEATE TERNS IN EUROPE

PLATE 9

Photo: Irish Tourist Board

CLIFFS OF MOHER, CO. CLARE

Birds normally return to their breeding places in early April and vacate them in July, but do not disperse to any great distance.

There is one inland record: a bird was found dead in May on Lough Neagh.

Puffin: *Fratercula arctica*

Summer visitor. Rarely seen in winter.

The most densely populated breeding stations are Tearaght, Skelligs and Puffin Island off Co. Kerry; the Bull Rock off Co. Cork; Great Saltee off Co. Wexford; Rathlin Island off Co. Antrim; Tormore and Horn Head, Co. Donegal; the cliffs of north Mayo, Stags of Broadhaven, Bills Rocks, Blackrock and Clare Island off Co. Mayo. In restricted areas of the Cliffs of Moher, Co. Clare, Puffins are abundant. They are not known on the coasts of Cos. Galway, Down or Waterford. The only east coast colonies are on Lambay and Ireland's Eye.

A general decrease has been noticed since 1925 and in some colonies this continues.

The numbers at Great Saltee fell greatly between 1912 and 1930, but a slight increase took place between 1960 and 1964; the present strength is about 1,500 pairs. In 1955 at least 20,000 pairs were estimated on Tearaght, rather fewer on Puffin Island. In 1965 at least 5,000 pairs were breeding on Great Skellig.

Puffins appear off their breeding stations early in March and come ashore at the end of that month. Departure starts in mid-July, by mid-August all have left.

The birds move away from the vicinity of the coasts in October and November. A southward movement along the west coast is noticeable then. Very few are seen in winter. Storm-driven birds are occasional far inland.

Pallas's Sandgrouse: *Syrrhaptes paradoxus*

Occurred in the irruptions of 1863 and 1888. Two further records.

During the 1863 irruption specimens were obtained in June in Cos. Dublin, Fermanagh and Donegal. One flock of about fourteen was reported.

The invasion of 1888 was more extensive. In May and June birds reached the western seaboard in Cos. Clare, Galway and Mayo. Further waves of immigrants arrived in July and November. Occurrences were widespread; several flocks of fifteen and sixteen were recorded.

There is a record of two shot in Co. Kildare in October 1876 and two remained for over a week in May 1954 in sandhills beside Wexford Harbour.

Stock Dove: *Columba oenas*

Resident. Probably winter visitor.

Stock Doves were first recorded in Ireland in 1875 and breeding established in 1877. Thereafter the spread was gradual and the bird now breeds in most counties. Since 1951 the breeding range has extended to the Dingle Peninsula in Co. Kerry and to western and northern Mayo.

On the Copeland Islands, Co. Down, where breeding is annual, the nests are in rabbit burrows and also on the cliffs. In 1963 a pair bred on Cape Clear Island, the first known breeding record there.

Stock Doves have been obtained at the lighthouses on Tuskar Rock off Co. Wexford and Maidens off Co. Antrim in October and November. At Saltee birds have been recorded thrice in May, once in September. Parties of up to six birds occur in spring and autumn on Cape Clear Island.

Flocks of over twenty-five birds are rarely seen.

Rock Dove: *Columba livia*

Resident.

The Rock Dove is widely distributed on the coasts and marine islands. It is more numerous on the north and west than on the south and east coasts.

In many areas, even in remote districts, Rock Doves have become interbred with feral stock and the influence of domestic blood is widely noticeable. In June 1965 there was a flock of 86 pure wild stock at Maharees, Co. Kerry.

Although the reason is not very clear, there has been a marked decline in numbers in very recent years, especially on the south-east coast, and this has been attributed, but without actual proof, to the effects of toxic seed-dressings.

Woodpigeon: *Columba palumbus*
Resident. Winter visitor.

Woodpigeons breed numerously in every county, their breeding range extending to the western seaboard. Cape Clear, Co. Cork, was colonised in 1963. In Connemara Woodpigeons have increased and spread and they are now found on the Mullet, Co. Mayo, in autumn.

In western maritime districts nests are often placed in stunted bushes.

Immigrants often arrive at the end of September, more often in early October; successive waves of immigration occur later, especially in severe winters or in years of particularly abundant beech-mast.

Winter visitors leave in February and March.

Evidence is far too meagre to allow of any deduction being made as to the origin of immigrants: one had been ringed in northern Britain and one in Denmark. One ringed at Great Saltee in April 1960 was shot in Wales in September 1960.

Turtle Dove: *Streptopelia turtur*
Scarce summer visitor which breeds irregularly. Passage migrant.

A few Turtle Doves spend much of each summer in southern coastal counties, particularly in Co. Cork, and also in the eastern ones. Even in Connacht there are a few records of birds having stayed from June to August: in no case was breeding suspected.

A pair bred at Clontarf, Co. Dublin, in 1939. Shortly afterwards a few pairs nested in north Co. Dublin for several years and after an absence did so again for three years from 1955. Breeding in another locality was suspected in 1960. In 1962 a pair bred in Co. Wicklow.

The bird is a regular passage migrant from the end of April to mid-June, sometimes in July, on all coasts, but in largest numbers off Co. Wexford where flocks of up to twenty are recorded on Great Saltee. Passage along the west coast is meagre.

Autumn passage in smaller numbers is noticed in August, September and early October.

At times of passage birds are occasionally seen inland, even in the western counties.

There are records of the bird in every month except February.

Collared Dove: *Streptopelia decaocto*

Resident since 1959.

Collared Doves were first known in Ireland in 1959. By the end of 1964 they had been recorded in eighteen counties and were known to be breeding in the following fifteen:—1959, in Dublin and Galway; 1960, in Down; 1962, Offaly, Fermanagh and Cork; 1963, Wicklow, Wexford and Antrim; 1964, Waterford, Kerry, Mayo, Armagh, Derry; 1965, Donegal.

In Co. Dublin since they first bred in Glasnevin Cemetery they are now well established in the city's northern suburbs and are breeding since 1962 at Baldoyle, and probably at Portrane and Balbriggan in 1964. In Co. Down the first were seen in 1959, breeding took place in 1960 and is now established in about five other localities. In Co. Galway a pair nested near Galway city in 1959; birds are now nesting in the city. In Co. Offaly they nested at Tullamore in 1962; at least four pairs were breeding there in 1964. It has only been reported in Co. Fermanagh from near Enniskillen where a pair has bred since 1962. In the vicinity of Cork city pairs are breeding in several places, the first recorded nesting was at Ballinacurra, in 1962; in 1965 it was breeding at Timoleague. The bird became established in Co. Antrim in 1963 and is well established in several parks in Belfast. In Co. Wicklow, having arrived in 1963, breeding took place in Greystones; numbers are increasing there and in the neighbourhood. It now breeds in Wicklow town. In Co. Wexford several pairs have bred in the city since 1963 and the bird is increasing; it is now breeding at Rosslare. A pair appeared in Co. Waterford in 1963 at Dungarvan; in 1964 two pairs bred there. Birds had been seen near Newport, Co. Mayo, in 1963, numbers increased there in 1964 and breeding was inferred; in 1965 it was breeding in Belmullet. First noticed in Co. Armagh at the end of 1963; breeding established in 1964. In Co. Derry the first was seen in 1964 and breeding takes place in at least one area in Derry city. In 1964 a pair bred in Tralee, Co. Kerry. In 1965 in Co. Donegal there was circumstantial evidence of breeding near Malin and Bundoran.

There are scattered records, other than of the breeding birds, usually of individuals, in Meath, Dublin, Wicklow, Wexford, Waterford, Cork, Kerry, Mayo, Offaly, Roscommon, Galway, Sligo, Donegal, Down, Monaghan and Armagh.

The largest flocks have been noticed in Belfast, maximum seventy-five birds; in Tullamore, twenty-five and in Wexford city fifteen.

Cuckoo: *Cuculus canorus*

Summer visitor.

The Cuckoo is widely distributed. It breeds in every county and on the larger marine islands.

It haunts bare mountain sides and the desolate regions of the extreme west as plentifully as cultivated areas. Numbers have decreased during the present century, even more noticeably recently. A Cuckoo has been recorded on April 2nd; there are several records for the first half of April; the second half is the normal time of arrival.

Departure of adults begins in July; young normally leave in August but juveniles have been killed at Irish light-stations in July and some in September.

The latest dates recorded are November 2nd and 26th.

The Meadow Pipit is the chief fosterer in Ireland.

Great Spotted Cuckoo: *Clamator glandarius*

Two records.

One was caught about March 1842 on Omey Island, off the Co. Galway coast. One was found dead in the early spring of 1918 near Cahirciveen, Co. Kerry; it was said to have been accompanied for about a week by another.

Yellow-billed Cuckoo: *Coccyzus americanus*

Three or four records.

One killed near Youghal, Co. Cork, in 1825 is in the National Museum. One was obtained in 1832 near Bray, Co. Wicklow. One was seen at Keel on Achill Island, Co. Mayo, on September 30th 1964, and it or another ten miles away on October 1st.

Black-billed Cuckoo: *Coccyzus erythrophalmus*
One record.

One was shot on September 25th 1871 at Killead, Co. Antrim.

Barn Owl: *Tyto alba*
Resident.

The White-breasted Barn Owl (*Tyto alba alba*) is resident and generally distributed, breeding in suitable places in every county and on some remote islands.

A decrease was noticed about 1950. Since 1960 this has been very marked and the Barn Owl is now absent from many of its former haunts.

After the breeding season the birds retire to woods and thickets.

The Dark-breasted Barn Owl (*Tyto a. guttata*) has been obtained thrice. One was killed near Thurles, Co. Tipperary, in January 1932. In the same year two were killed early in April in Co. Kerry; one at Listowel, the other near Tralee.

It is very probable that others of this Continental race visit Ireland undetected.

Scops Owl: *Otus scops*
Nine records.

One was obtained in July a few years previous to 1837 at Loughcrew, Co. Meath. One was killed in April 1847 near Kilmore, Co. Wexford. In June 1852 one was obtained, probably in Co. Wexford. About March 1853 one was shot at Hillsborough, Co. Down. On November 17th 1883 one that had been present for some days was captured in Belfast. On May 31st 1889 of two present one was obtained at Foulkesmill, Co. Wexford. About May 20th 1899 one was captured in Connemara, Co. Galway. On May 6th 1907 a male was captured at Fastnet lighthouse, Co. Cork. In July 1911 one was obtained at Ballyliffin, Co. Donegal.

Snowy Owl: *Nyctea scandiaca*
Irregular visitor to 1950; one record since.

Up to about 1950 the Snowy Owl was an irregular but fairly

frequent visitor. There were fifty records of its occurrence before 1950, but only one since, in January 1956 in Co. Antrim.

Occurrences have taken place in every month except August, the majority in December.

The bird has been reported in all four provinces and in eighteen counties, including some inland ones. It has appeared most often in the north and north-west, especially on the Mullet, Co. Mayo. Of the total reports, twenty-two have come from Co. Mayo, Donegal follows with seven, then Galway with five.

Little Owl: *Athene noctua*

Three records.

One was killed at Kilmorony, Co. Kildare, in June 1903, having been there since February. One was washed ashore while still alive near Larne, Co. Antrim, in the autumn of 1945. One was seen on Great Saltee, Co. Wexford, on May 4th 1960.

Long-eared Owl: *Asio otus*

Resident. Possible passage migrant and/or winter visitor.

This owl breeds in every county, being thinly distributed where suitable woodlands exist.

Its range extends to the western seaboard.

Some increase has been reported with the spread of conifer plantations.

Occasionally it has been reported in autumn and winter at lighthouses, at Cape Clear in March and October, at Copeland in July and September.

In other coastal localities several together in autumn have probably been passage migrants or immigrants.

Short-eared Owl: *Asio flammeus*

Has bred. Winter visitor.

A pair attempted to nest on the Mullet, Co. Mayo, in 1923. Breeding was first proved in May 1959 when a nest with eggs, from which three young were reared, was found in Co. Galway. Breeding was not repeated.

In 1959 single birds were reported in Co. Antrim in May, Co.

Donegal in July and two together in Co. Wicklow in July. In each case observation of the birds was on one day only. There have been a number of records of the bird in May, June and July. Occurrences have been in every month: the months October to February supply the majority of records.

In winter this owl is thinly and irregularly distributed in suitable areas, more frequently near the coasts than far inland. Numbers fluctuate considerably from year to year.

Migrants have been seen at Cape Clear, Co. Cork, Great Saltee, Co. Wexford, and Tory Island, Co. Donegal, both in spring and autumn.

Nightjar: *Caprimulgus europaeus*

Summer visitor. Perhaps passage migrant.

The Nightjar is irregularly and very locally distributed, but is more general in Munster and Leinster than elsewhere.

With the possible exceptions of Longford, Leitrim and Monaghan, it breeds in every county. In Co. Galway Nightjars breed at Carna and perhaps near Clifden and Ballynahinch. Since 1893 the breeding range has extended to include western Mayo, even Achill Island. It breeds in the north of Donegal but not in the west. Breeding on the Dingle Peninsula in Kerry and in west Clare remains to be proved.

Arrival is usually recorded in early May, sometimes in late April. Departure takes place in September, the latest date known being 30th.

There are records of Nightjars striking Skelligs and Tuskar Rock lighthouses in June, and of one at Blackrock off Co. Mayo in October.

Swift: *Apus apus*

Summer visitor. Perhaps passage migrant.

Swifts breed in every county and are often numerous in towns. Numbers in western districts have increased since 1932, indeed increase has been general.

In 1955 it was found breeding in limestone cliffs at Knockmore, Co. Fermanagh.

The earliest date for spring arrival is April 19th at Great Saltee.

There are nine reports of Swifts between April 20th and 24th, usually of single birds, but on April 20th 1949 of ten together in Co. Mayo. Early reports came from widely separated localities in 1949, 1954 and 1962.

The first week of May is the usual time of regular arrival; movement continues in early June. Late June and July observations of migrating birds, if not of passage migrants, are perhaps of birds making mid-season movements. Such movements of parties moving westward or arriving from the south have been noticed on the coasts of Wexford and Cork in several years. On July 13th in two hours over 500 Swifts flew south-west in a mountain valley near Belfast and in the last week of July a daily arrival from the north has been witnessed at Ballycastle, Co. Antrim.

Departure is in August; stragglers are seen in September, more rarely in October.

Alpine Swift: *Apus melba*

Nine records.

One was shot off Cape Clear, Co. Cork, about midsummer 1829. One, obtained at Rathfarnham in Co. Dublin on March 14th 1833, is in the National Museum. One was shot at Doneraile, Co. Cork, in June 1844 or 1845. One was picked up near Lough Neagh in May 1866. One came in over the sea at Bray Head, Co. Wicklow, in August about 1920. In May 1933 one, in company with Swifts, was seen near Kilmeadow, Co. Waterford. On April 13th 1938 one was seen at Killiney, Co. Dublin. One was present at Great Saltee, Co. Wexford, on September 14th and 15th 1958. One was seen at Ballycotton, Co. Cork on August 6th and 7th 1965.

Needle-tailed Swift: *Chaetura caudacuta*

One record.

One was seen at Cape Clear, Co. Cork, on June 20th 1964.

Kingfisher: *Alcedo atthis*

Resident.

Kingfishers breed in every county, but in several they are local and very scarce. The bird is found chiefly in lowland districts.

Reports of marked decrease have recently come from some localities, but the decrease does not seem to be general.

There is a local movement to the coasts in autumn and in severe weather and this may help to offset the danger of casualties in severe winters. Birds return to their breeding haunts in March. On two occasions, in July and in September, single birds have been killed at isolated light-stations.

[Belted Kingfisher: *Ceryle alcyon*

Two records.

Two specimens in the National Museum were obtained in 1845: one of them was shot in Co. Meath on October 26th, the other in November in Co. Wicklow where it had been present for some days. At the time they were considered to be genuine vagrants, but later have not been admitted as such due to the possibility that they were 'escapes'. In the light of present-day views, there is the distinct possibility that they could have been genuine vagrants.]

Bee-eater: *Merops apiaster*

Vagrant.

There are thirteen records, mainly from maritime counties in the south and east. On one occasion seven were seen together in Co. Cork, on another six together in Co. Wicklow. Two together were seen in Co. Cork in April 1955; all other records have been of single birds.

Occurrences have taken place in every season of the year; the majority have been in May.

Roller: *Coracias garrulus*

Vagrant.

Fourteen have been recorded. Where dated, three occurrences have been in spring—April and May; seven in autumn—September and October.

All reports have been of single birds and took place in the Cos. Cork (2), Wexford (3), Donegal (2), Clare, Kerry, Kildare, Leitrim, Sligo and Antrim (one each); one in the 'south of Ireland'.

The most recent record is that of one in May 1958.

Hoopoe: *Upupa epops*
Passage migrant.

Since 1953 the Hoopoe has been recorded annually in spring and autumn. There are many February records, but most are for March and May, rather fewer in April; there are one or two for June and July. In autumn most occur in September and October. One was seen in Co. Down on November 7th 1959. A Hoopoe was seen at Union Hall, Co. Cork, on December 15th 1961; one that spent three weeks previous to January 17th 1962 near there could have been that same bird. One stayed for several days around January 7th 1962 at Bantry, Co. Cork.

Unprecedented numbers visited Ireland between March 28th and April 8th 1965. At least forty-two individuals were reported chiefly in Cos. Cork (16) and Wexford (6), but also in Waterford, Kerry, Galway, Mayo, Donegal and in the inland county of Tipperary.

Occurrences are most frequent in Cos. Cork and Wexford. It rarely reaches Co. Kerry. There are records for all counties except Meath, Longford, Leitrim, Monaghan and Tyrone.

Inland the Hoopoe has been seen in Limerick, Tipperary, Kilkenny, Cavan, Armagh, Carlow, Kildare, Leix, Offaly, Westmeath, Roscommon and Fermanagh.

A pair frequented a locality in Co. Waterford during the summer of 1934. Breeding was suspected but fell just short of proof.

Green Woodpecker: *Picus viridis*
Three records.

One was obtained at Sallymount, Co. Kildare, on September 27th 1847; one at Rathmullen, Co. Donegal, in January 1854; one about which there are no further details was obtained 'in the last century' at Kilshrewley near Granard, Co. Longford.

None of the above specimens is known to exist.

Great Spotted Woodpecker: *Dendrocopos major*
Irregular visitor.

There are over fifty-five records of this woodpecker. It has been recorded in every county except Longford, Westmeath, Leitrim, Cavan, Tyrone and Donegal. Most instances have been of single birds, but in one case two and in another three were together.

Occurrences have ranged from September to May, the majority in November, followed in order by February, October and December, lastly January.

The winter of 1949–50 was marked by a visitation during which birds were reported in Cos. Dublin, Tipperary, Down, Armagh, Cork, Offaly and Antrim. Four were recorded in northern Ireland on dates between February 12th and April 8th.

A pair was present in Glenshesk valley, Co. Antrim, in 1931 from April 10th to 22nd.

A female shot in Co. Fermanagh on December 12th 1959 was referable to the race *Dendrocopos m. anglicus.*

The following specimens have been assigned to the northern race (*Dendrocopos m. major*): one from Kilkeel, Co. Down; a male from Co. Galway; a female from Co. Waterford and a male from Co. Antrim.

Wryneck: *Jynx torquilla*

Vagrant.

Twenty-seven Wrynecks have been recorded. Records have been far more frequent in recent years since the establishment of Bird Observatories, at which nearly all occurrences since 1950 have taken place. All occurrences have been on or near the coasts and especially in the south. Two were in spring (April and May), twenty-five in the period August to November, the majority in September (sixteen records). The November instance was of one obtained on 14th in 1925 in Co. Cork.

Short-toed Lark: *Calandrella cinerea*

Vagrant as drift migrant.

There are sixteen records, with one exception, when there were two together, of single birds.

Three occurrences have been in May, two in August, six in September and five in October.

The first recorded in Ireland was shot off the Mayo coast in October 1890. Since 1951 (except in 1952 and 1964) it has been reported each year; there were two occurrences in 1955 and 1956.

The three May occurrences and the majority of the rest have been at Great Saltee (8 birds); in addition four others have been seen in Co. Wexford, one at Tory Island, Co. Donegal, one at Duncrue Street marsh, Belfast, and one at Cape Clear, Co. Cork. One was present on Inishtrahull from October 17th to 21st 1965.

Six of the birds have shown the characteristics of the race *Calandrella c. brachydactyla*.

Lesser Short-toed Lark: *Calandrella rufescens.*

Four records.

The four records concern a total of about forty birds. A flock of about thirty were closely watched in sandhills beside Tralee Bay, Co. Kerry, on January 4th 1956. Five were seen on Great Saltee, Co. Wexford, on March 30th 1956. Two were observed at Annagh, near Belmullet, Co. Mayo, on May 21st 1956. Five were present on Great Saltee on March 22nd 1958 and until at least 25th.

Woodlark: *Lullula arborea*

Has bred. Since 1927 eight records.

Formerly the Woodlark was locally resident in Munster, Leinster and Ulster.

At least one pair bred in Co. Wicklow in 1894 and one pair in Co. Wexford about 1905.

Then in 1954 a pair bred successfully near Rosscarbery, Co. Cork, and two other adults were present. No birds returned in subsequent years.

Two Woodlarks were seen in sandhills at Portmarnock on the Dublin coast on September 4th 1927. Single birds were seen on October 15th and 26th 1951, November 4th 1954, March 30th 1956 at Great Saltee, Co. Wexford. One was identified near Swords, Co. Dublin, on April 3rd 1960. One was seen on Cape Clear Island, Co. Cork on September 2nd 1965.

Skylark: *Alauda arvensis*

Resident. Passage migrant. Winter visitor.

Skylarks breed commonly in suitable localities throughout the country and on marine islands. A decrease has been noticed during the past five years.

The migrations tend to be confusing. In spring there is no evidence of migration at Saltee from March to June: at Cape Clear spring migration is very meagre in March and April only. Migration has been recorded at Inishkea off the Mayo coast in March and April and at Tory Island in April.

Passage migration in autumn is heavy, many hundreds being on the move for days at a time, especially in October. Large numbers have been watched arriving in north-east Ireland and in the same period hundreds depart southward from the coast of Wexford. This movement takes place on a broad front as birds are noticed traversing the country in inland areas. Considerable numbers arrive at Malin Head, Co. Donegal, from over the sea; at about the same time Cape Clear experiences a movement out to sea to the south-west and southward. This movement continues on a reduced scale in November.

At the same time that the movements just described are in progress, there is migration to the north and north-west, especially noticeable on the Wexford coast, but also in some inland areas. This movement probably concerns immigrants coming to winter.

The number of winter visitors is often increased when weather outside of Ireland is severe. Skylarks then pour into the country; it has been noticed that when conditions improve the birds immediately leave again.

It is unknown what proportion, if any, of our breeding stock emigrate. It seems probable that they do no more than move from exposed places to more cultivated areas.

Alauda a. theresae is the name that has been given to birds collected in the west of Ireland.

The Eastern Skylark (*Alauda a. intermedia*) is represented by three specimens in the National Museum. All were obtained at light-stations: Old Head of Kinsale, Co. Cork, on October 7th 1910; Tuskar Rock, Co. Wexford, on October 5th 1911; Inishtrahull, Co. Donegal, on March 12th 1915.

Shore Lark: *Eremophila alpestris*

Four records.

One was obtained at Wicklow Head on November 4th 1910. An

adult male frequented the west pier at Dun Laoghaire, Co. Dublin, from April 2nd to 13th 1950. One, believed to have been a female, was closely watched near Kilcoole on the Co. Wicklow coast, on December 8th 1950. There were two together at Tacumshin Lake, Co. Wexford, on February 9th 1964 in a winter that was remarkable for the widespread occurrences and numbers of these birds reported in Britain.

Swallow: *Hirundo rustica*

Summer visitor. Passage migrant. Occasional in winter.

Swallows breed in suitable places in every county and on many marine islands. Nests have been found in caves on Clare Island, Achill and the Cork coast.

There are indications of some decrease, at least locally.

March 2nd is the earliest known date for spring arrival; there are numerous reports of Swallows in March. Early April is the normal time of first appearance, most come at the end of April and in early May. There is passage in May and June.

The majority arrive on the south-east coast and spread westwards across the country.

Flocks are on the move as early as mid-July; movement becomes more intense in August and September, continues in October with stragglers in November.

Emigration is most noticeable on the south-east coast and for many days on end hundreds are seen passing.

In late summer roosts containing thousands of birds are found in reed beds.

There are December records in Cos. Dublin and Cork; in the latter county a number was seen regularly near Glandore in 1959. In January 1913 several were seen in Co. Kerry.

Red-rumped Swallow: *Hirundo daurica*

One record.

One was watched for considerable periods on April 10th and 11th 1952 at Great Saltee, Co. Wexford.

House Martin: *Delichon urbica*

Summer visitor. Occasional in winter.

This species breeds in every county, but its distribution is local. It nests on one or two marine islands. The breeding range extends to the very far west, where colonies are often of a very few pairs. In some localities colonies containing fifty to a hundred nests are found. A recent increase in numbers has been noticed.

Nesting on sea-cliffs is known in Cos. Cork (about 50 pairs at Power Head in 1964), Waterford, Wicklow (at least 30 pairs in 1965), Dublin, Antrim, Derry and Donegal.

In some desolate western regions nests are found in haybarns and cow-sheds.

Nesting under bridges has been reported in several places.

House Martins arrive only rarely at the end of March, seldom in early April, chiefly from mid-April to early June, most in May.

Departure is from late, rarely early, August to October with stragglers later. Most emigrate in September.

Arrival and departure is most in evidence on the south-east coast.

Single birds have several times been seen in November, twice in December.

Sand Martin: *Riparia riparia*

Summer visitor.

Sand Martins breed in every county and on some marine islands off the west coast.

In a widely scattered survey the largest colonies were two of 150 pairs, six were of over 100 pairs, the average for twenty-four colonies being about 66 pairs.

Nesting colonies of a few pairs are sometimes found in the face of turf banks; in one case the colony was of 50 pairs. Sometimes nesting takes place in crevices in ancient buildings or waterside quays, or in drainage holes in concrete walls. There is a record of a colony in holes drilled for placing explosives in a stone bridge.

The earliest spring arrival date is March 12th; there are reports for 14th, 16th and 17th in different years. The end of March is the usual time for arrival and birds continue to arrive in May, sometimes in early June.

Photo: Northern Ireland Tourist Board

LOUGH ERNE, CO. FERMANAGH, BREEDING HAUNT OF COMMON SCOTERS AND GARDEN WARBLERS

Top photo: Ian Finlay
Lower two photos: David Cabot

RUINS. THREE TYPICAL BREEDING PLACES OF TREE SPARROWS

Departure is from the end of August to early October with stragglers as late as November 11th.

Numbers seen migrating on the coast in autumn are small, many less than in spring at which period movement is more concentrated.

One winter record refers to a bird seen on January 12th in Co. Kildare.

[**Purple Martin:** *Progne subis*
One record.

A female was shot near Dun Laoghaire, Co. Dublin, a short time previous to March 1840. The specimen is in the National Museum. The record is included here in consideration of the comment in *British Birds*, 48: 9.]

Golden Oriole: *Oriolus oriolus*
Irregular visitor, chiefly in May.

There have been about sixty records in the months April, June and 'in summer', the great majority in May (24); one in October.

Most reports have been of single birds, but in four cases two were together; once five together and once 'a small flock' was reported.

Most Golden Orioles have appeared in maritime counties, chiefly those in the south. Inland records have come from Limerick (1), Kildare (1), Kilkenny (1), Roscommon (1) and Tyrone (2).

Raven: *Corvus corax*
Resident.

Ravens have increased considerably during the present century. They breed locally on coastal cliffs, marine islands and in mountain ranges.

Nests are occasionally found on trees, and are increasingly reported. In Co. Wicklow a pair are known to have nested in trees for about five years. The nest has once been found on the sloping ground of a mountain top.

In autumn and winter Ravens wander far from their usual haunts. There is no evidence of overseas migration.

Following the breeding season, flocks (maximum recorded fifty-six birds) are sometimes seen.

In Co. Dublin in May a roost contained twenty-two birds.

Carrion Crow: *Corvus corone*

Probable resident. Scarce regular winter visitor. Perhaps passage migrant.

Carrion Crows have been increasingly reported in recent years. The bird has bred in Cos. Mayo and Down. In 1956 it attempted to breed in Co. Kerry.

Probably cases of breeding are overlooked.

Interbreeding with Hooded Crows has occurred in Cos. Dublin, Down and Antrim.

Carrion Crows are seen most often in the north-east; in May 1964 a flock of thirteen was counted in Co. Down. In recent years reports have come from Cos. Kerry, Wexford, Wicklow, Dublin, Limerick, Antrim, Derry and Donegal. In Co. Cork this crow is repeatedly reported at Cape Clear Island; in Co. Dublin there were four occurrences in 1959. In September 1964 six were reported, and in early October six together, in widely separated localities in Co. Wexford.

The presence of breeding stock makes it difficult to give occurrences by months. Since 1950 there are reports for every month. By far the majority are seen in September (15) and October (10), many of the instances being at Cape Clear and on the Wexford coast. As records in July and August, November and December are few, those for September and October are perhaps of migrants.

Hooded Crow: *Corvus cornix*

Resident.

This crow is numerous and widespread, breeding in every county and on marine islands.

In recent years it has noticeably increased and is extending its range into western Donegal where in 1950 it was rare; there too it is increasing.

After the breeding season flocks form and increase in size in winter when parties of fifty birds are not unusual. The maximum known size of a flock is ninety-four, in Co. Cork.

In Co. Kerry a roost consisting of fifty-eight birds has been reported.

There is no evidence of immigration or emigration.

Rook: *Corvus frugilegus*

Resident. Winter visitor. Probably passage migrant.

Rooks breed in every county where there are trees or bushes. Though the size of rookeries has decreased in many places due to the felling of trees, there has been no noticeable decrease in the total number of birds. Relatively few rookeries exceed fifty pairs.

Rooks wander to the larger marine islands during the breeding season, more regularly from July onwards. Dispersal follows breeding.

There is a cross-channel migration in spring and autumn. Vast immigratory movements in autumn have occasionally been witnessed in south-western coastal localities.

In winter immigration resulting from severe weather occurs. At such times Rooks reach the larger islands off the west coast.

At any season Rooks may be found in the most desolate regions where no trees exist within twenty miles.

Jackdaw: *Corvus monedula*

Resident.

Jackdaws breed increasingly in every county. They nest in towns, ruined buildings, old castles, in hollow trees and cliffs both inland and marine, even on the western seaboard. Few breed on the western marine islands but about fifty pairs nest on Great Saltee, Co. Wexford, and on the east coast Lambay and the Copeland Islands have colonies.

Magpie: *Pica pica*

Resident.

Magpies breed in every county and where no high trees exist they nest in low bushes. The breeding range does not nowadays extend to remote marine islands, though stray birds occasionally visit them.

In Achill and on the Mullet Magpies breed. On the Dingle Peninsula numbers have fluctuated. Between 1940 and 1950 the bird was rare there though in 1938 so numerous that forty-one were seen in a flock. Since 1950 it has again increased and is now considered plentiful.

Magpies are found nesting in cities.

Flocks occur at times. Thirty to forty birds together have been seen; a flock of forty-six was reported in October in Co. Down, one of fifty-two in February. A flock of eighty has been recorded and roosts of over a hundred birds are known.

Magpies first appeared in Ireland, in Co. Wexford, about 1676.

Jay: *Garrulus glandarius*
Resident.

The Jays in Ireland are of the race *Garrulus g. hibernicus.*

Since 1900 the bird has continued to spread and is still increasing. It breeds in all counties except Kerry, Sligo, Leitrim, Donegal and Derry, but very locally in some others. Only quite recently the breeding range has come to include Co. Mayo. As yet nesting is unknown west of the large Connacht lakes, though in woods west of Lough Mask individuals are seen regularly in winter.

Chough: *Pyrrhocorax pyrrhocorax*
Resident.

The Chough breeds on many precipitous coasts and marine islands, especially in the south and west. Always its distribution is somewhat local.

Formerly breeding on inland mountain cliffs was regular, but with the decline in its numbers nearly all such haunts were abandoned.

A recovery of numbers began about 1925. This continues and the Chough is more than holding its own and breeding is again taking place inland in two places in Co. Kerry, two in Co. Clare and one in Co. Donegal.

A census between 1960 and 1964 showed that there were between 567 and 682 pairs in Ireland.

There is no evidence of migration other than of a purely local character.

After the breeding season a few Choughs are being seen increasingly several miles inland.

Great Tit: *Parus major*

Resident. Probably winter visitor.

Our breeding birds belong to the race *Parus m. newtoni* and are widely distributed in every county. Great Tits breed on the Dingle Peninsula in Co. Kerry, but are rare in Connemara at all times, even where there are woods. Breeding is unknown on Achill Island.

An increase has been noticed in Co. Wexford in September and in Co. Mayo in October. Great Tits have been reported in October at light-stations off the coasts of Wexford and Cork. At Cape Clear Great Tits appear regularly in varying numbers up to twelve in a day, chiefly in October, but with records between August 26th and November 1st.

Of about twelve that arrived on Great Saltee on October 9th 1957 two remained until April 1958. They were no doubt birds connected with the irruption of the species in autumn 1957. Several that were trapped showed the characters of the Continental race *Parus m. major*; probably all were of that race. Nine flew west past Saltee on October 10th. This invasion was also noted in Co. Kerry and on the east coast.

Blue Tit: *Parus caeruleus*

Resident. Perhaps winter visitor or passage migrant.

Of the tits in Ireland the Blue Tit (*Parus c. obscurus*) has the widest range. It breeds in every county in desolate as well as wooded areas. Though its range reaches the western seaboard, it is not resident on marine islands other than Cape Clear, Achill and Lambay. To others it is an occasional visitor.

Blue Tits have been reported at isolated light-stations in April and October. In one case in October a bird rested for a while on Coningbeg light-vessel off the south Wexford coast then departed southward.

At Cape Clear Island migrant Blue Tits have been recorded in August, September and October, the maximum in a day being twelve.

In September and October 1961 migrants were noted at Erris Head, Co. Mayo, and a large influx at Malin Head, Co. Donegal. There were exceptional numbers in Co. Dublin in October of that year.

The influx at Malin Head seems to be an annual event in October; in different years about forty have been recorded on October 3rd and 6th and at least thirty on 21st. Some of these birds were seen flying at an unusual height.

In August 1957 one at Saltee, Co. Wexford, and a day maximum of over six in October were probably connected with the invasion of Britain that autumn.

It is not known to what race these migrants belonged.

Coal Tit: *Parus ater*

Resident. Occasional autumn visitor.

The so-called Irish Coal Tit (*Parus a. hibernicus*) is resident and generally distributed except in the north-east of the country. There its place is taken by the British Coal Tit (*Parus a. britannicus*) which race is found in many localities throughout Ireland.

Extension of breeding range has kept pace with the increase in conifer plantations. This tit has spread to the Dingle Peninsula and western Connemara. It has bred in Achill since 1900.

The Coal Tit is more dependent upon woodland habitat than are the Great and Blue Tits.

Single birds of the Continental race *Parus a. ater* have been identified on Cape Clear Island, Co. Cork, on October 6th 1959 and October 13th 1961.

Long-tailed Tit: *Aegithalos caudatus*

Resident. Possibly occasional winter visitor.

Breeding in every county the Long-tailed Tit is found in all but treeless districts. A nest was found near Tralee in 1956 but so far there is no evidence of breeding on the Dingle Peninsula, where in December 1954 a party of seven was the first record for that area.

As a result of severe weather, numbers have at times been greatly reduced, the species continuing scarce for two or three years.

On rare occasions small flocks have visited desolate headlands and marine islands in October. A flock of five visited Great Saltee on November 5th 1959; two trapped were considered to be *A. c. rosaceus*, which is our breeding race.

October 1961 was notable for records showing some movement: a single bird at the Copeland Islands, Co. Down, fourteen at Culdaff, Co. Donegal, thirty coasting westwards at St. John's Point, Co. Down, on 18th, eighteen on 19th. In November numbers in Co. Dublin were reported above normal. On December 15th there were four on North Aran Island off Co. Galway.

Treecreeper: *Certhia familiaris*
Resident.

The Treecreeper is generally distributed in suitable localities and breeds in every county. In the west its range extends to the limit of wooded areas.

Our breeding birds are of the race *Certhia f. britannica* but the name Irish Treecreeper (*C. f. meinertzhageni*) has been given to a local form found in Co. Kerry. It has richer rufous upper-parts than *britannica* and other plumage characters which seem to be almost constant.

Treecreepers have occurred single once at Cape Clear in June, at Maidens lighthouse in August and at Great Saltee in September. In 1960 single birds were seen at Copeland Island on six days between July 31st and September 30th, one bird on August 31st 1961. In no case was the race ascertained.

Wren: *Troglodytes troglodytes*
Resident. Spring and autumn migrant.

The Wren breeds throughout Ireland, even in desolate regions, on the most remote marine islands and on mountain tops. For no apparent reason it has ceased to breed on Great Saltee since 1955.

Migration is noticeable at isolated stations in spring and autumn, but its nature is as yet obscure.

At Tory Island, Co. Donegal, Wrens pass in small numbers in

April and early May and in October; at Inishtrahull, Co. Donegal, in October and November. At Saltee, Co. Wexford, there is a light passage at the end of March and in April; more marked in October. Many arrive on the island, perhaps to winter, in November.

In April one was seen as it circled M.V. *Inishfallen* when at sea three miles off the coast of Cork.

Dipper: *Cinclus cinclus*

Resident.

The Dipper is widely scattered where suitable streams occur. It nests in every county, though very scarce in several. In many areas it is extremely local or absent from streams with much suitable habitat.

It is rare in some of the western areas of Co. Mayo and absent from many places in south-west Cork.

Our resident birds are of the Irish race (*Cinclus c. hibernicus*).

A dipper showing the characters of the Black-bellied form (*Cinclus c. cinclus*) was seen on the River Tolka, Co. Dublin, in January and early February 1956. One showing these characters was seen at Tory Island, Co. Donegal, on October 13th 1962.

Mistle Thrush: *Turdus viscivorus*

Resident. Winter visitor.

The Mistle Thrush was first recorded in Ireland in 1808. It breeds plentifully in every county and nowadays even as far west as Achill and the Mullet.

In treeless areas it often nests on stone walls and buildings; the nest has been found on the ground.

Small flocks form at the end of June. A large immigration is noticeable on all coasts in September, October and November. This immigration is very obvious at Malin Head, Co. Donegal, where about 600 were watched arriving over the sea on October 22nd 1961.

Nestlings ringed in Scotland and northern England have been recovered here in winter.

There is emigration in February and March.

Fieldfare: *Turdus pilaris*
Winter visitor.

Fieldfares are widespread in winter. In some winters they are abundant, in others relatively scarce.

Since they prefer open and upland districts, Fieldfares are more plentiful west of the River Shannon and, in general, are more numerous in the north than in the south of the country.

When severe weather prevails farther east, greater numbers visit Ireland.

The earliest arrival date is September 7th. The main body of immigrants arrives in November and leaves at the end of April. Birds have been seen as late as May 31st.

Single birds have been seen on July 14th and 21st, three on August 17th. It is likely that they may have summered in Ireland. The state of moult of an adult collected in Co. Galway on August 14th 1924 indicates that the bird must have summered here.

Young ringed in Scandinavia have been recovered here in winter. A migrant ringed at Great Saltee in November was recovered in Norway in the following May.

Song Thrush: *Turdus philomelos*
Resident. Partial migrant. Winter visitor.

Song Thrushes breed in every county; they nest in the most desolate western districts and on many remote marine islands; on Inishbofin off Co. Galway only since 1951.

Commencing in September there is a heavy immigration which continues into October and November. These immigrants come largely from Scotland and northern England.

When weather conditions farther east are severe, further influxes come to Ireland in winter.

Our breeding birds belong to the race *Turdus p. clarkei*. A small proportion in the west cannot be separated from a small proportion of the Hebridean race (*T. p. hebridensis*). A bird showing the characteristics of that race was caught in Co. Tipperary on January 1st 1963. Similar birds arrive at Malin Head, Co. Donegal, in October.

Birds of plumage intermediate between *T. p. clarkei* and *T. p. philomelos* have been examined at Great Saltee in November and in Co. Mayo.

Redwing: *Turdus iliacus*

Passage migrant. Winter visitor.

Redwings of the typical race *Turdus i. iliacus* are common throughout the country, though numbers fluctuate.

They are far more plentiful in the western half of Ireland than in the eastern and are relatively scarce in east coast counties.

The majority arrive in November, but immigration commences in mid-October. After November influxes in the form of weather movements take place, augmenting the numbers already present and raising the numbers to be seen in the east of Ireland.

The heavy immigration on the east coast is of birds of the typical race.

The earliest known dates for arrival in autumn are August 26th (Co. Down) and September 20th (Co. Dublin). Departure commences in March, the last Redwings are seen in mid-April. A single bird was seen at Tory Island, Co. Donegal, on May 1st, another on May 8th.

In May 1951 a pair attempted to breed in Co. Kerry.

The Iceland Redwing (*Turdus i. coburni*) is a passage migrant and winter visitor.

As a result of observations at Tory Island and Malin Head, Co. Donegal, and Erris Head, Co. Mayo, it is now known that the Icelandic race occurs regularly, often in considerable numbers, along the west coast in autumn. There is a return migration along that coast in April.

The autumn migrants may be immigrants, but also birds on passage for birds of this race are recorded at Cape Clear, Co. Cork, in October and a specimen was obtained in October at Great Skellig, Co. Kerry.

This race is not plentiful in Ireland in winter so that possibly many of these autumn migrants are on passage. Ringed birds of Icelandic origin have, however, been recovered in winter in widely separated counties.

Ring Ouzel: *Turdus torquatus*
Summer visitor. Passage migrant.

The Ring Ouzel has decreased as a breeding bird since 1900. It breeds very locally in Co. Kerry, northern Tipperary, Cos. Wicklow, Waterford, Leix, Sligo, Fermanagh, Down, Derry, Tyrone and Donegal, and perhaps Limerick and Antrim.

There have been records of arrival in March (earliest on 4th) and early April, but most come in mid-April and passage continues into early May. Autumn emigration and passage takes place from the end of August (once early August) to early November.

At Great Saltee, through which it passes regularly in spring and autumn, the maximum present on a single day was fourteen on April 2nd 1956.

At Cape Clear very small numbers move through in spring and autumn; it is a regular migrant at Roche's Point, Co. Cork. There are records for May and October at Tory Island, Co. Donegal.

Occurrences in winter were rare in the past, the last recorded being in January 1918.

Blackbird: *Turdus merula*
Resident. Winter visitor.

Blackbirds breed numerously in every county and do so on isolated islands off the west coast.

Within this century the Blackbird established itself as a breeding species in western Donegal, on the Dingle Peninsula and Valentia Island, Co. Kerry, the Mullet, Co. Mayo, and has become more numerous generally.

There is an immense migration, noticed chiefly on the Co. Wexford coast, sometimes commencing in September, more usually in October, reaching its climax in November, when at Great Saltee 1,000 have been present on a single day.

In 1960 a heavy influx took place in Co. Kerry on August 28th and 29th, increasing on 31st and followed next day by a marked decrease. The significance of this movement is not clear.

Most immigrants come from Scotland, northern England, Scandinavia and Denmark.

Our breeding stock is chiefly sedentary or subject to dispersal movement only.

A first-winter female ringed at Saltee in September 1958 was caught at Kilmore Quay, on the adjacent mainland, in June 1960 when breeding there. For at least four further years it bred and wintered there.

White's Thrush: *Turdus dauma*
Three records.

Three have been shot: one near Bandon, Co. Cork, in early December 1842; one in the spring of 1867 at Ballymahon, Co. Longford; one near Westport, Co. Mayo, on January 9th 1885. The last is in the National Museum.

American Robin: *Turdus migratorius*
Six records.

One was obtained at Shankill, Co. Dublin, on May 4th 1891, one at Lough Gill, Co. Sligo, about December 7th 1892, one in Co. Leitrim in December 1894. An adult male was seen on three days between December 10th and 18th 1954 at Camolin, Co. Wexford. A male was seen on January 11th and 13th 1955 at Blennerville, Co. Kerry. One came aboard a trawler off Skelligs, Co. Kerry, on January 28th 1965.

Olive-backed Thrush: *Hylocichla ustulata*
One record.

One was picked up dead on May 26th 1956 at Blackrock lighthouse, Co. Mayo. The skin was sent to America where it was critically examined and found referable to the eastern race *Hylocichla ustulata swainsoni*.

Wheatear: *Oenanthe oenanthe*
Summer visitor. Passage migrant. Occasional in winter.

Our breeding birds are of the race *Oenanthe o. oenanthe* and are widely distributed throughout all maritime and mountainous regions. They are less plentiful and very local in the central counties, thus very few nest in Co. Cavan and breeding in Cos. Longford and Westmeath is doubtful.

It appears that some decrease has taken place locally in recent years.

The earliest record of a Wheatear in spring is of one in Co. Clare on February 3rd, but there is the possibility that it had wintered.

Arrival takes place in mid-March, sometimes early in that month. The majority arrive in April and chiefly on the Wexford coast. Migration continues until mid-May. Birds depart from early August to mid-October, the majority in September. Passage continues into October with stragglers recorded in November.

There are several winter records, the last being of one in Co. Dublin during December 1957 and January 1958.

The Greenland Wheatear (*Oenanthe o. leucorrhoa*) is a spring and autumn passage migrant on all coasts. The earliest spring record is for April 13th. Normal passage is from the end of April, heaviest in May. Return passage is from the end of August until the end of September; stragglers occur in October.

The Faeroe/Iceland Wheatear (*Oenanthe o. schiøleri*) has been recorded in September as have been intermediate birds.

Black-eared Wheatear: *Oenanthe hispanica*

One record.

A male of the black-throated form of the western race, *Oenanthe h. hispanica*, was collected at Tuskar Rock lighthouse, Co. Wexford, on May 16th 1916. The specimen is in the National Museum.

Black Wheatear: *Oenanthe leucura*

One record.

One was closely watched on June 10th 1964 at Portnoo, Co. Donegal.

The field description does not, however, exclude the possibility that the bird was a White-crowned Black Wheatear (*Oenanthe leucopyga*) in its black-crowned form.

Stonechat: *Saxicola torquata*

Resident. Partial migrant. Perhaps passage migrant.

Stonechats are widely distributed and breed in every county. They are most plentiful in coastal districts.

Severe winters have from time to time reduced numbers drastically, especially in inland districts. Recovery to normal numbers is slow.

Some Stonechats emigrate in October and early November. One ringed at Cape Clear, Co. Cork, in September was found in Spain the following November.

Return migration takes place from February until early May.

Marine islands such as Cape Clear and Inishbofin are deserted in winter. It seems more likely that their populations emigrate rather than that they move to the mainland, where also in winter numbers diminish.

Migration is very noticeable at Malin Head, Co. Donegal, in autumn.

Whinchat: *Saxicola rubetra*

Summer visitor. Probable passage migrant. Occasional in winter.

The distribution of the Whinchat is extremely local. Following a decrease in many localities, the population is again showing a rapid upward trend and the breeding range extending.

Since the end of last century breeding distribution has changed considerably. At present it breeds numerously only in Co. Kildare, though up to 1900 there was no record for that county. In Co. Kerry a few pairs breed on the Dingle Peninsula and locally elsewhere. In Co. Cork breeding is erratic; very few breed spasmodically in Co. Wexford. It is a scarce bird in Co. Wicklow; in Co. Dublin it breeds very occasionally, if at all. A very few nest in Co. Offaly, but Whinchats now breed in Cos. Meath and Leix. Few breed in Co. Longford but they do so nowadays commonly in Co. Westmeath. The breeding range includes Co. Roscommon; of Cos. Sligo and Leitrim there is no recent information. A pair bred on Achill Island, Co. Mayo, in 1961. It is again increasing in Co. Donegal. A few nest in Co. Antrim, including Rathlin Island. In

Co. Fermanagh a few breed. A pair bred in Co. Clare in 1956 and in Co. Down in 1957 but not more recently.

For other counties there is no up-to-date information.

During post-breeding dispersal and at times of migration Whinchats are seen inland in counties where they do not breed.

Whinchats normally arrive at the end of April (earliest date recorded, March 17th), most in early May. The majority leave in September, though migration is in progress at the end of August and in October.

Whinchats are noticed regularly in spring and autumn on the coasts of Co. Down, on the Copelands and on the Cos. Wicklow and Wexford coasts under conditions suggestive of passage migration.

There are records of the bird on November 29th, in December, January and February.

Redstart: *Phoenicurus phoenicurus*

Scarce irregular summer visitor. Passage migrant.

The Redstart bred in Co. Wicklow from 1885 to 1890; in Co. Tyrone for several years up to 1895; several pairs were reported to have bred in one locality in Co. Kerry in 1946; in 1955 it bred in Cos. Antrim and Tyrone; in 1959 and 1960 at one locality in Co. Wicklow.

Spring passage from mid, occasionally early, April to May 21st is regular at Saltee, along the east coast, at Copeland off Co. Down where one was recorded on June 7th. At Tory Island it occurs occasionally in spring and autumn and in autumn in northern, eastern and western coastal localities and in appreciable numbers at Cape Clear, Co. Cork.

Autumn passage occurs from the end of August to mid-October, with stragglers to November 15th.

Black Redstart: *Phoenicurus ochruros*

Passage migrant.

The Black Redstart is recorded more frequently than was the case before 1900.

It is seldom found far inland, though there are reports of it in Cos. Tyrone, Leix, Kildare, Limerick, Galway, Kilkenny, Tipperary and Offaly.

Passage and immigration is noticed chiefly on the east and south-east coasts, but also on all other coasts. At Cape Clear, Co. Cork, it is regularly reported. At Great Saltee it has once been seen on August 25th and rarely at the end of September, most are observed regularly in October and there are a number of November records.

Migration is reported from March to May, again chiefly on the east coast. There is one record for June 15th.

Small numbers winter annually, chiefly in eastern coastal counties. In Limerick city several did so for a number of winters.

Nightingale: *Luscinia megarhynchos*

Ten records.

Single birds at Great Saltee, Co. Wexford, on May 11th 1953 during a period of easterly weather; May 13th and 24th 1954; May 6th 1956; September 8th and 13th 1958; May 11th and 22nd 1959; May 15th 1960, this bird was in song. One was in song at night on May 6th and 9th 1955, at Carton, Co. Kildare.

Bluethroat: *Cyanosylvia svecica*

Eight records.

Singly at Great Saltee, Co. Wexford, September 27th 1954; April 15th and 16th (same bird); September 11th 1956; at Cape Clear, Co. Cork, September 17th; October 17th 1959; August 28th and October 23rd 1960; at Great Saltee, August 30th 1961.

Robin: *Erithacus rubecula*

Resident. Partial migrant. Passage migrant.

Our breeding birds are of the race *Erithacus r. melophilus*. They are found in all types of country, even at 1,500 feet above sea-level. They are abundant in Connemara and nest on the Mullet and many marine islands.

A proportion of the population of the more exposed marine islands vacates them in winter.

Migration takes place from the end of February to the end of March, rarely in April and May and from the end of August (occasionally mid-August) to October or November. The nature of these migrations is obscure, but passage migration is almost certainly involved. Migration is most in evidence on the east coast and then in autumn. A hundred Robins in a day have several times been recorded at Great Saltee in September. With the exceptions below, all trapped there have been *E. r. melophilus*.

The Continental Robin (*Erithacus r. rubecula*) has thrice been handled at Great Saltee, Co. Wexford (May 22nd 1957, May 4th 1958 and October 11th 1962). About fifty were reported at Cape Clear, Co. Cork, on October 9th 1959, at a time when a large number of this form arrived in the Isles of Scilly.

Two Robins trapped in Co. Tipperary on January 5th 1963 had the characters of this form.

Grasshopper Warbler: *Locustella naevia*

Summer visitor.

Grasshopper Warblers breed in many localities, in no county more widespread than in Waterford and in no place more numerously than near Portumna, Co. Galway.

Since 1900 the breeding range has expanded and the bird probably breeds in every county.

Nowadays nesting occurs in the extreme west of Cos. Mayo and Donegal, on the Dingle Peninsula and the coastal belt of north-west Kerry.

Spring arrival has several times been noted on April 11th; most arrive in early May. One was killed at Maidens lighthouse, Co. Antrim, on July 29th.

Departure starts in September (rarely at the end of August) and continues into early October: latest date October 15th.

Migration is confined almost exclusively to the east coast.

Pallas's Grasshopper Warbler: *Locustella certhiola*

One or two records.

A male found dead at Rockabill lighthouse off Co. Dublin on

September 28th 1908 is in the National Museum. A warbler almost certainly of this species was seen at Great Saltee, Co. Wexford, on May 12th 1954.

Great Reed Warbler: *Acrocephalus arundinaceus*
Two records.

One was found dead near Castletownshend, Co. Cork, on May 16th 1920. One was seen on Cape Clear Island, Co. Cork, on June 14th and 15th 1964. The description of this last does not entirely rule out the possibility that the bird could have been *A. stentoreus.*

Reed Warbler: *Acrocephalus scirpaceus*
Has bred. Vagrant.

The only known case of breeding was when a nest containing five eggs was found at Monlough, Co. Down, in May 1935.

One was in song near Portaferry, Co. Down, on June 21st 1956.

The Reed Warbler has been recorded on migration thrice in spring (April 22nd, May 9th and 26th), over twenty times in autumn (August 30th to November 3rd), chiefly in September.

Most occurrences have taken place at Great Saltee, Co. Wexford, and Cape Clear, Co. Cork, where six have been recorded on one day. Most reports have been of single birds. One was found dead as far north as Maidens lighthouse, Co. Antrim, on May 26th.

At both Great Saltee and Cape Clear 'unstreaked' *Acrocephalus* warblers have been frequently reported. It is highly probable that they were of this species.

In some cases Reed and Marsh (*A. palustris*) Warblers are inseparable. No definite occurrence of the latter is known in Ireland.

Sedge Warbler: *Acrocephalus schoenobaenus*
Summer visitor.

Sedge Warblers breed plentifully in every county and on some marine islands.

First arrivals appear in mid-April (early date April 5th). The main arrival is in the second week of May. Most leave in August, many in September, the latest known date being November 9th.

Migration is most in evidence on the Wexford coast.

A bird at Inishtrahull lighthouse, Co. Donegal, on September 16th and perhaps some of those seen after mid-September may indicate passage.

Aquatic Warbler: *Acrocephalus paludicola*

Seven records.

An immature male was obtained at Bull Rock lighthouse, Co. Cork, on September 20th 1903. A female was found dead at Tuskar Rock lighthouse, Co. Wexford, on August 9th 1913. One was closely watched on Achill Island, Co. Mayo, on June 2nd 1906. One was seen at Great Saltee, Co. Wexford, on September 2nd and one on October 1st 1958, another on August 28th 1961. One was seen at Cape Clear, Co. Cork, on August 31st 1961.

Melodious Warbler: *Hippolais polyglotta*

Annual migrant in autumn.

Up to 1954 there were only three authentic records. Since 1956 this warbler has been recorded annually, occurrences being chiefly at Cape Clear, Co. Cork (19), and Great Saltee, Co. Wexford (12).

One was trapped at Erris Head, Co. Mayo, on September 8th 1961 and one at Copeland, Co. Down, on August 20th 1962.

Occurrences have ranged from August 11th to October 7th, the majority in September (19); August (8); October (3).

Since 1956, between one and fifteen have been reported each year.

Icterine Warbler: *Hippolais icterina*

Annual migrant in autumn. One record in spring; one in summer.

Up to 1914 this warbler had been twice recorded. None was then reported until 1955 since when one to ten are recorded each year. Most have been seen at Cape Clear, Co. Cork (29), and at Great Saltee, Co. Wexford (11), where a number have been trapped. One has been reported at Copeland, Co. Down, one at Old Head of Kinsale, Co. Cork. It has been recorded in August (8) (earliest, 15th), September (27) and October (4) (latest, 13th).

One was trapped at Great Saltee on May 17th 1964; one was obtained in Co. Dublin on June 8th 1856.

In every autumn up to about five individual *Hippolais* warblers are seen, chiefly at Cape Clear, which cannot be specifically identified and are therefore recorded as Melodious/Icterine Warblers.

Olivaceous Warbler: *Hippolais pallida*

One record.

One was trapped at Tory Island, Co. Donegal, on September 29th 1959. It was referable to the race *Hippolais p. elaeica.*

Blackcap: *Sylvia atricapilla*

Summer visitor. Passage migrant. A few winter regularly.

The Blackcap is extremely local in its distribution. Co. Wicklow is its chief stronghold. In Co. Cavan it breeds beside Lough Ramor and Lough Sheelin, perhaps near Killeshandra, but nowhere plentifully. In recent years circumstantial evidence points to breeding in Donard and Tollymore Parks near Newcastle, Co. Down. It is highly probable that several pairs are breeding nowadays at Shane's Castle and Belfast Castle, Co. Antrim. A very few may breed in Co. Wexford. An amazingly isolated breeding place is at Curragh Chase, Co. Limerick, where at least two pairs were breeding in 1964, but nothing about past years is known.

There are widespread reports of males in song but without indication of breeding.

The presence of wintering birds makes determination of exact dates of spring arrival uncertain, but certainly arrival sometimes takes place at the end of March and in early April. Most arrive in the second half of April and early May.

Autumn migration lasts from the end of August until early November.

Much of the migration on our coasts is that of birds on passage. Such movement has been noted at Copeland, Co. Down, Tory Island, Co. Donegal, and off the Connacht coast.

A number of Blackcaps winter each year, especially in Dublin suburbs and in Co. Wicklow, but may do so almost anywhere.

A male ringed in Austria in August 1961 was found dead in Co. Wicklow on December 14th 1961.

Barred Warbler: *Sylvia nisoria*

Irregular autumn passage migrant.

There are nineteen records of the Barred Warbler. Occurrences have been on the east, west and south coasts, once, in October, at Inishtrahull on the north coast. Most have been seen at Great Saltee, Co. Wexford, and on dates between August 23rd and October 10th.

Garden Warbler: *Sylvia borin*

Summer visitor. Passage migrant. One winter record.

This warbler is very local in its distribution. A habitat adjacent to a lake seems essential.

On the wooded shores and islands of Lough Ree it is common. Elsewhere in the Shannon valley Garden Warblers breed very locally beside Loughs Derg and Bofin, their range extending to Lough Key. In Co. Cavan Garden Warblers nest beside several lakes and do so around Lower Lough Erne and to a less extent at Upper Lough Erne, Co. Fermanagh. It has bred spasmodically in the past in Cos. Cork, Clare, Sligo, Leix. In 1956 a pair bred in Co. Down. A pair bred at Curragh Chase in Co. Limerick in 1964—a surprising outpost in the breeding range.

Birds arrive at their breeding haunts in early May.

Autumn migration is noted occasionally in early August, chiefly from early September to early October. Passage migration is observed at Great Saltee in spring and autumn. Records at isolated stations on the north-east, north, north-west and west coasts point to passage migration in autumn, much less marked in spring.

A Garden Warbler was seen on February 18th 1960 at Blackrock, Co. Dublin.

Whitethroat: *Sylvia communis*

Summer visitor.

Wherever there is rough cover Whitethroats are common, even in desolate regions, on headlands and marine islands. Though numbers fluctuate at times, there is some evidence of a general decrease in recent years.

Whitethroats commence to arrive in mid-April (early dates March 14th 1902, 21st, 1900); the heaviest migration is in May. At Great Saltee 500 have been recorded in one day.

Autumn migration is less marked, most birds moving in September, with stragglers to October 20th. There is one record for November 9th.

Arrival and departure take place almost entirely on the south and south-east coasts. Stragglers at both seasons have occurred rarely off Cos. Donegal, Mayo, Galway and Kerry.

Lesser Whitethroat: *Sylvia curruca*

Scarce autumn migrant; occasional in spring.

There are thirty-eight records of the Lesser Whitethroat. Since 1951 one to seven have been reported annually except in 1955 and 1958. Numbers have shown an increase in the past few years, no doubt due to the establishment of observatories.

Most have been seen at Cape Clear, Co. Cork (19), and Great Saltee, Co. Wexford (12). There are single records for Cos. Kerry, Dublin, Wexford (Tuskar Rock), Down, Antrim and two for Donegal. In Down the bird was trapped at Copeland on September 14th 1964, an autumn in which no less than five occurred at Cape Clear.

There are records of two birds (at Great Saltee) on April 29th, in May (7), June 1st (1), August (1), September (16), October (9), November (2).

A Siberian Whitethroat (*Sylvia c. blythi*) was trapped at Great Saltee on November 15th 1954.

Subalpine Warbler: *Sylvia cantillans*

Four records.

One was found dead at Hook Tower lighthouse, Co. Wexford,

on September 17th 1933. An adult male was found dead at Maidens lighthouse, Co. Antrim, on June 13th 1937. A first-winter female was trapped at Great Saltee, Co. Wexford, on September 10th 1954. A first-winter bird was seen at Cape Clear, Co. Cork, on October 6th and 7th 1962.

Dartford Warbler: *Sylvia undata*
One record.

A female referable to the race *Sylvia u. dartfordiensis* was caught at Tuskar Rock lighthouse, Co. Wexford, on October 27th 1912.

Rufous Warbler: *Agrobates galactotes*
Two records.

One shot at the Old Head of Kinsale, Co. Cork, in September 1876 was of the nominate form *Agrobates g. galactotes.*

One seen on Great Saltee, Co. Wexford, from September 22nd to October 4th 1951 was considered to belong to one of the races *A. g. syriacus* or *A. g. familiaris.*

Willow Warbler: *Phylloscopus trochilus*
Summer visitor. Passage migrant.

Willow Warblers are common and are more generally distributed than the Chiffchaff.

They breed in every county and even on the western seaboard, but not on marine islands.

Considerable numbers arrive in early April (one record for March 30), the main body in mid-April. Migration continues until mid-May; a few are still moving in June.

Departure commences at the end of July. Most leave in August. Migration lasts into September with stragglers well into October.

The Northern Willow Warbler (*Ph. t. acredula*) is a regular passage migrant in spring. It has been identified on all coasts, chiefly in the east and regularly at Great Saltee in May when up to fifteen have been seen on one day.

Greenish Warbler: *Phylloscopus trochiloides*

Nine records.

One was obtained at Great Saltee, Co. Wexford, on August 25th 1952. One was trapped at Great Saltee on September 19th 1957. At Cape Clear Island, Co. Cork, one was present from October 17th to 24th 1959, one on October 14th 1961, one October 8th to 12th 1962, single birds on September 25th, October 10th and November 4th in 1964. One was present on Inishtrahull, Co. Donegal, from October 18th to 21st 1965.

Chiffchaff: *Phylloscopus collybita*

Summer visitor. Passage migrant. Occasional in winter.

About 1850 the Chiffchaff was breeding in only seven counties; less than fifty years later it was breeding in all. Chiffchaffs now breed commonly in wooded districts throughout the country.

In some western districts they still are scarce, but quite recently have spread in north-west Kerry and nested near Tralee in 1960.

Arrivals in early March are fairly common, the majority come in the second week of April. Migration on a reduced scale continues into May. A migrant was seen on Inishvickillane off Co. Kerry on June 11th 1965. Autumn migration lasts from the end of August to mid-October with stragglers to mid-November.

Some Chiffchaffs probably winter annually in Ireland, especially in Cos. Cork and Kerry. They have been reported in December, January or February in Cos. Wexford, Wicklow, Dublin, Tipperary, Fermanagh, Leitrim, Sligo, Derry and Down.

Some of these wintering birds may well be 'northern' Chiffchaffs.

Birds of the Scandinavian race (*Phylloscopus c. abietinus*) and/or the Siberian form (*Ph. c. tristis*) have been recorded as 'northern' Chiffchaffs at Great Saltee in September, October and November. Some have been identified as definitely of the former race. A bird of the Siberian race was killed at Eeragh Island lighthouse, Co. Galway, on November 25th 1943, another at Tuskar Rock lighthouse, Co. Wexford, on October 14th or 15th 1946.

A Chiffchaff ringed at Great Saltee on April 7th 1956 was retrapped there on April 14th 1957 and was evidently using the same migration route in successive seasons. Chiffchaffs do not breed on Great Saltee.

Wood Warbler: *Phylloscopus sibilatrix*

Has bred. Vagrant.

The Wood Warbler has bred in Cos. Cork, Wicklow, Leix, Galway and Down, the most recent case being in Cork in 1938. What have almost certainly been unmated males have been heard in song in six or seven scattered counties.

At present it is considered to be an irregular vagrant, reported chiefly at Cape Clear, Co. Cork, in August and September. One was trapped at Copeland Island, Co. Down, on May 12th 1963.

Bonelli's Warbler: *Phylloscopus bonelli*

Two records.

One at Cape Clear, Co. Cork, September 2nd 1961. One at Great Saltee, Co. Wexford, from September 1st to 16th 1962.

Arctic Warbler: *Phylloscopus borealis*

Two records.

One was trapped at Tory Island, Co. Donegal, on September 1st 1960. One was seen at Cape Clear, Co. Cork, on August 29th 1961.

Yellow-browed Warbler: *Phylloscopus inornatus*

Vagrant in autumn.

This warbler has been reported on about fifteen occasions. One was shot on Tearaght, Co. Kerry, in October 1890. Further records have all been since 1952 and almost annually. They have taken place at Great Saltee, Co. Wexford (3), Copeland, Co. Down (2), Malin Head (1) and Tory Island (2), Co. Donegal, Inishbofin, Co. Galway (1) and Cape Clear, Co. Cork (5). Most instances have been of single birds.

Numbers were above normal in 1960 when there were three at Cape Clear on September 27th, seven or eight, possibly nine being present during the next few days. Saltee recorded one on September 28th.

Dates have ranged from August 6th to October 14th, most records in October.

Goldcrest: *Regulus regulus*
Resident. Winter visitor.

The Goldcrest is plentiful, being found wherever there are woodlands or even a few conifers. Its range includes the Dingle Peninsula, Connemara and Achill Island.

There is a very large immigration in autumn, with, in some years, great 'rushes'.

Migration commences in August but is more marked in September and October and chiefly on the east coast. It is noticed on a small scale at western marine islands and at Cape Clear.

Two hundred and one hundred have been recorded at Great Saltee on days in early October.

Return migration starts in March and increases throughout April. There are records from lighthouses of Goldcrests in summer.

Continental Goldcrests (*Regulus r. regulus*) have been identified in March, April, May, September, October and November off the east and south-east coasts.

Firecrest: *Regulus ignicapillus*
Nine records, concerning about 24 birds.

One was found dead near Glengarriff, Co. Cork, on December 7th 1943. About five were seen in a hedgerow on Valentia Island, Co. Kerry, on October 4th 1951. At Cape Clear, Co. Cork, there were seven on October 10th 1959, one October 21st 1960, one September 27th 1961, one on October 5th 1962 and a small influx from October 8th to 11th 1964; most on 9th (7); one November 20th to 22nd 1964.

Spotted Flycatcher: *Muscicapa striata*
Summer visitor.

Spotted Flycatchers are widely distributed but somewhat local.

They breed in every county. Numbers fluctuate; in some summers the bird is scarce.

Its range includes the Dingle Peninsula and the westernmost woods in Connemara and Achill; in western Donegal it is scarce.

The earliest recorded date is of one in Co. Wexford on March 12th; also on the Wexford coast one was seen on April 19th. Normally the summer visitors are present from May to September, the majority arriving between early May and early June. Over a hundred on a day have been seen at Great Saltee but much smaller numbers are more normal.

Inland, loose flocks of up to twenty birds form in July and August but have gone by mid-September.

Autumn migration lasts from August to the end of September with stragglers to mid-October. Numbers seen migrating in autumn are smaller than in spring.

At Tory Island, Co. Donegal, individuals have been seen on October 9th and 12th; at Fastnet, Co. Cork, on October 20th and one struck Tuskar Rock lighthouse, Co. Wexford, between November 20th and 30th.

Brown Flycatcher: *Muscicapa latirostris*

One record.

At Great Saltee, Co. Wexford, on September 6th 1957 one was identified and considered to be a first-winter bird.

As this species is extensively imported into Britain, the possibility that the bird was an 'escape' cannot be ruled out. It is significant, however, that a Barred Warbler, a bird not listed among importations, arrived at Saltee the same day.

Pied Flycatcher: *Muscicapa hypoleuca*

Passage migrant.

The Pied Flycatcher is regular on autumn passage; fairly frequent but less regular in spring.

Most of the occurrences have been coastal and particularly at Great Saltee, Co. Wexford and at Cape Clear, Co. Cork. Pied Flycatchers have, however, been recorded on passage along the east coast from Copeland, Co. Down, to Tuskar Rock, Co. Wexford; irregularly at several points on the north coast and at a number along the west coast, in particular Tory Island. Here and there along the south coast other than at Cape Clear it has been reported.

Spring occurrences have taken place in April but the majority in May.

In autumn the dates have ranged from August 20th to October 19th; most are seen in September.

The maxima reported in a day are twenty-five at Cape Clear, fifteen at Great Saltee.

A pair was seen at Holywood, Co. Down, on June 11th, 12th and 20th 1953; a female at Stormont, Belfast, on August 3rd 1953.

Single Pied Flycatchers have been reported far inland only near Athenry, Co. Galway, in September 1928 and 1930.

Red-breasted Flycatcher: *Muscicapa parva*

Almost annual on autumn passage.

Nowadays in most years between one and six are reported in September and October, dates ranging from September 6th to October 13th.

The majority of reports come from Cape Clear and Great Saltee, in addition one from Tory Island and one from Malin Head.

Before the establishment of Bird Observatories there were scattered records of birds obtained irregularly at lighthouses on the south-east, south and west coasts.

One was seen near Glenealy, Co. Wicklow, on July 8th 1961, but not subsequently.

Hedge Sparrow: *Prunella modularis*

Resident. Passage migrant.

Hedge Sparrows nest commonly in every county. Their range extends to bleak, treeless districts and to the larger marine islands.

There is evidence of what may be passage migration on a small scale in May, much more marked in September and October.

Since there is no noticeable increase in numbers in winter, it seems improbable that these migrants are immigrants.

A male and female obtained in Co. Antrim in November 1934 appeared referable to the Hebridean Hedge Sparrow (*Prunella m. hebridium*).

Richard's Pipit: *Anthus novaeseelandiae*

Five records.

One was captured at Lucan, Co. Dublin, on November 22nd 1907. One was caught at Kilbarrack, Co. Dublin, on October 23rd 1911. One was seen at Carnsore Point, Co. Wexford, on November 5th and 6th 1954. One was seen near Tramore Strand close to Horn Head, Co. Donegal, on August 19th 1955. One was seen at Cape Clear, Co. Cork, on October 13th 1961.

Tawny Pipit: *Anthus campestris*

Eight records.

One was seen on Great Saltee, Co. Wexford, on May 11th 1953 during a spell of strong easterly winds. One seen on Great Saltee on April 21st 1954 was probably the same bird as that seen on 23rd and 26th. One was seen at Duncrue Street marsh, Belfast, Co. Antrim, on May 21st 1957 during a period of easterly winds. One was seen at Great Saltee on September 18th 1958. At Cape Clear, Co. Cork, one was seen on October 9th 1959; one on October 12th 1961; one September 27th 1962; an immature bird, October 17th 1963.

Meadow Pipit: *Anthus pratensis*

Resident. Passage migrant. Winter visitor.

The Meadow Pipit of the typical form *Anthus pratensis pratensis* is a widespread resident which breeds in every county and on marine islands.

Following the breeding season Meadow Pipits vacate the more exposed regions and move to lowland marshes and coastal areas. There is as yet no evidence that any emigrate. Weather movements occur within the country.

This form is a passage migrant in October and early November and in spring.

It is possible that there is a small immigration in autumn.

A decrease in numbers has taken place during the past fifteen years.

The race *Anthus pratensis theresae* having its origin in Iceland is an abundant passage migrant on all coasts. The autumn passage lasts from mid-August to mid-October, being at its height in the second half of September and in early October. At this period this race traverses Ireland and throughout the country large flocks are seen on the move.

Birds of this race ringed when on autumn migration at Saltee have been recovered in France, Portugal and Spain.

A small number remains to winter in Ireland. Spring passage is well marked in March and April, especially in mid-March.

Tree Pipit: *Anthus trivialis*

Passage migrant.

Passage is regular but in very small numbers, in May, exceptionally at the end of April (early date, April 8th at Cape Clear), and from mid-August to early October.

This passage is most noticeable on the Wexford coast and at Cape Clear, Co. Cork, but single birds have been reported on the north and east coasts and at Tory Island and Malin Head, Co. Donegal.

There are only three records of the bird in inland localities: one in song on May 21st 1914 near Portumna, Co. Galway; one, clearly an unmated male, was in song between May 15th and July 10th 1932 near Athenry, Co. Galway; one in song on April 29th 1959 in Co. Antrim.

Red-throated Pipit: *Anthus cervinus*

About eight records.

One was seen at Great Saltee, Co. Wexford, May 2nd 1955. At Great Saltee in 1956 single birds were seen on September 4th, 8th to 10th, 11th to 13th, 17th and 18th; there were two on 14th and 15th, and three on 16th. Three together were seen at Great Saltee on September 1st 1958 and one was trapped there on August 28th 1961.

Rock Pipit: Water Pipit: *Anthus spinoletta*

Rock Pipit: *Anthus spinoletta petrosus*

Resident.

This pipit is generally distributed on rocky coasts and marine islands.

There is no evidence of migration other than of a very local character. Dispersal and feeding movements cause numbers to fluctuate locally.

A single Rock Pipit was seen inland at Lough Ennell, Co. Westmeath, on September 27th 1959.

The Scandinavian Rock Pipit (*A. s. littoralis*) has been once identified, at Tory Island, Co. Donegal, on April 14th 1961.

The status of this race in autumn and winter is impossible to ascertain since these pipits cannot then be sub-specifically separated.

There is one record of the American Pipit (*A. s. rubescens*). One was present at Great Saltee, Co. Wexford, from October 8th to 16th 1951, during which period it was repeatedly trapped.

Water Pipit: *Anthus spinoletta spinoletta*

Two records.

One was shot at Rockabill, off Co. Dublin, in June 1861. One was seen on the North Bull, Co. Dublin, on March 18th 1943.

Pied Wagtail: White Wagtail: *Motacilla alba*

Pied Wagtail: *Motacilla alba yarrelli*

Resident. Passage migrant.

The Pied Wagtail has greatly increased during the century and is one of our most common and widespread passerines. It breeds in every county and on inhabited marine islands. It now nests on the Mullet and on desolate seaboards where formerly it was a winter visitor only.

There is passage, especially on the east and south coasts, from March to May and from August to October, but sometimes in early November.

There is a long-established winter roost of about 1,000 birds in trees in O'Connell Street in Dublin; in Belfast in one busy locality about 250 roost in some elm trees.

White Wagtail: *Motacilla alba alba*

Passage migrant.

White Wagtails are passage migrants in spring and autumn. They are more frequent on the west coast and the coasts of Cos. Antrim and Down in spring than in autumn; in some years more than usual are noticed in September on the coast of Kerry.

Passage on the east coast is observed at both seasons, but is more noticeable in autumn than in spring. Over a hundred have been recorded on one day in mid-September at Great Saltee, Co. Wexford.

At the end of March, especially in April and sometimes in May passage is in progress and again in August (rarely), September and October.

Inland records are few, but five were seen on Lough Carra, Co. Mayo, in September 1928; a party of six near Athenry, Co. Galway, in September 1944. Single birds have been seen in Cos. Mayo, Roscommon and Clare in April. Others have been reported in May on the shores of Lough Neagh and frequently at Lough Beg, Co. Derry, where up to sixty have been seen and where a few have been noted in autumn.

There have been occurrences in June, July and August. In June in Co. Mayo a bird was seen carrying nesting material and in Co. Wexford one was in song on July 7th, but without evidence of breeding.

Grey Wagtail: *Motacilla cinerea*

Resident. Passage migrant.

Grey Wagtails breed sparingly in every county, their distribution being very local. In some far western districts and some central counties the bird is scarce.

Local seasonal movements occur within the country.

Though in small numbers, there is evidence of migration in spring and autumn at Cape Clear, Co. Cork, Copeland, Co. Down, and in autumn, more rarely in spring, at Great Saltee, Co. Wexford.

Occasionally in spring migrants are seen at Tory Island, Co. Donegal, and in autumn both there and at Malin Head.

All these movements are clearly indicative of passage migration.

Yellow Wagtail: *Motacilla flava*

Yellow Wagtail: *Motacilla flava flavissima*

Scarce irregular summer visitor. Passage migrant.

In the last century this race of the Yellow Wagtail bred on the shores and islands of Loughs Corrib, Mask and Carra in Connacht. Numbers gradually diminished and breeding ceased about 1920.

Breeding haunts around Loughs Neagh and Beg were known since about 1850; here too numbers decreased until by 1942 there was none.

The only other known locality where breeding had taken place was in Co. Dublin in 1868.

No instance of breeding anywhere was known until 1956 when a pair bred beside Belfast Lough, Co. Down. A pair bred in 1957 in Belfast and three pairs near Larne, Co. Antrim, in 1958.

There was circumstantial evidence that a pair bred beside Lough Derg, Co. Tipperary, in 1962. In 1963 and 1964 a pair bred in Co. Wicklow, in 1965 two pairs; in 1963 the male showed some affinity to *M. f. flava*; in 1964 all the adults were typical *M. f. flavissima*.

As a passage migrant this wagtail is regular in small numbers in spring and autumn on the east coast; at Great Saltee, where as many as twenty were seen on September 24th 1954, and at Cape Clear.

On the west coast, since breeding in Connacht ceased, occurrences are irregular and usually of single birds in August and September.

Blue-headed Wagtail: *Motacilla flava flava*
Six or seven definite records.

A pair was seen and quite possibly bred, though absolute proof was lacking, near Larne Harbour, Co. Antrim, in 1958.

A male was seen at Cape Clear, Co. Cork, from October 23rd to 28th 1959. At Great Saltee, Co. Wexford, one was trapped on May 2nd 1960 and one seen on September 23rd 1961. In 1963 there was circumstantial evidence that a pair bred near Duncrue Street marsh, Belfast. A male was seen at Bog Meadows, Belfast, Co. Antrim, on August 22nd and 23rd 1963, and could have been that of the pair seen at Duncrue Street marsh. In 1965 a pair bred successfully in Co. Kerry.

Ashy-headed Wagtail: *Motacilla flava cinereocapilla*
One record.

Two pairs nested in the Belfast dock area in 1956, one pair doing so on reclaimed land at Duncrue Street, the other on reclaimed land at Sydenham; both places are adjacent to Belfast Lough. From their respective nests three and five young were fledged.

Grey-headed Wagtail: *Motacilla flava tunbergi*
One record.

A wagtail typical of this race was seen at Great Saltee, Co. Wexford, on May 2nd and 3rd 1960.

Waxwing: *Bombycilla garrulus*
Winter visitor.

Periodically large immigrations of Waxwings take place in winter. In other winters there have been smaller influxes.

During the present century the winters 1903–04, 1932–33, 1946–47 and 1957–58 were notable for the numbers that occurred. The winter 1946–47 stands out for the numbers recorded. Not only were the numbers remarkable, but also the number of counties visited and the large size of flocks seen. The largest numbers were reported in the northern counties, where flocks of up to forty-five birds were seen in various places. In one locality a hundred in a flock was noted. During the incursion in 1957–58 reports were even more widespread but numbers were not so great.

An immigration on an unprecedented scale took place towards the end of November 1965. The widespread reports included occurrences in all the western coastal counties.

Some of the largest flocks contained over 50 birds in Galway and Co. Meath, over 100 birds in north Co. Dublin.

A flock estimated to contain 300 birds was seen in Enniskillen, Co. Fermanagh.

Since 1955 no winter has passed without reports of a number of Waxwings.

Records have come from every county following the 1965 irruption.

The majority of reports have been from October to March, with three in April, one in May and in July and one or two in August.

Great Grey Shrike: *Lanius excubitor*
Vagrant.

This shrike had been reported at least twenty-eight times previous to 1900. Since then one was shot on March 23rd 1906 in Co. Meath. In 1957 two were recorded: one at Blackrock lighthouse, Co. Mayo, on June 19th and 20th and one at Tory Island, Co. Donegal, on June 21st.

There are authentic records of occurrences in fifteen counties and in all provinces: in Ulster (13), Leinster (13), Munster (3), Connacht (2).

The months where known have been January (4), March (2), June (2), August (3), October (1), November (2), December (5).

Lesser Grey Shrike: *Lanius minor*
One record.

An immature bird was seen on Cape Clear Island, Co. Cork, on September 14th 1962.

Woodchat Shrike: *Lanius senator*
Drift migrant in spring and autumn.

Up to 1950 only three single birds had been recorded, two in May, one in August, off the Co. Wexford coast.

From 1953 to 1961, except in 1956 and 1957, this shrike was recorded annually in spring and autumn at Great Saltee, Co. Wexford. One to six, on an average about three, were seen each year. Birds were most often seen in May and September, and usually during or following periods of easterly or south-easterly winds.

Often the birds would remain on the island for several days.

Ireland was without a record from 1961 until, in 1964, one was seen on Cape Clear Island, Co. Cork, on August 4th.

Red-backed Shrike: *Lanius cristatus*

Vagrant.

The Red-backed Shrike has been recorded on twenty-one occasions, sixteen of them in autumn, two in spring and three in June.

All records have been from or near the coast and most of them off the south-east and south coasts. There are two records from isolated west coast stations and one at Inishtrahull off the north coast.

An immature shrike seen at Cape Clear, Co. Cork, on October 9th and 10th 1962 was referable to one of the *isabellinus* group of Red-tailed Shrikes.

Starling: *Sturnus vulgaris*

Resident. Winter visitor.

After a remarkable decrease just previous to 1800 Starlings increased again about 1850 and extended their range, but for many years distribution remained irregular.

Starlings now breed in every county; the spread of their breeding range has further expanded since 1950 and they have nested since 1953 in the Tralee district of Co. Kerry where in 1943 the bird was unknown in summer. A pair bred on the Dingle Peninsula in 1955 and in 1959 a few pairs in Dingle. By 1963 it was breeding plentifully there.

In western Galway and Mayo too the breeding range has extended since 1959 and reached Inishbofin in 1962, Achill Island in 1965.

Since 1955 the increase has been noticeable in western Donegal.

Starlings breed on a few exposed marine islands.

After the breeding season considerable movement takes place within the country. The bird becomes scarce except in coastal regions and is especially scarce in the east midlands. But at the same time it is abundant far inland west of the Shannon valley and particularly in western coastal regions.

An enormous immigration takes place in autumn. It commences on a small scale at the end of August, increases through September, further in October, reaching its peak in November. These migrants arrive chiefly on the south-east coast. In November thousands in a day are seen arriving from the south-east; the maximum estimated in a day at Great Saltee being over ten thousand.

Severe weather conditions abroad cause further incursions and local weather movements.

Most of the winter visitors are breeding stock from Scandinavia, Denmark, some from Holland and a very few from north Germany and Poland; others come from northern Britain.

Winter visitors leave during March and up to mid-April.

Reed beds are most favoured for roosting; woods are often used, also sea-cliffs and caves. There are large urban roosts in Dublin, that on the Customs House being of about 3,000 at its maximum. In Belfast the largest of several is in the docks where 50,000 have been reported.

Rose-coloured Starling: *Sturnus roseus*

Irregular visitor.

This starling has been recorded about forty times, but at irregular intervals. There have been long periods without a report of the species. The two most recent records were of an adult at Great Saltee, Co. Wexford, September 25th to 28th 1954 and of an immature bird at Cape Clear, Co. Cork, August 31st to September 8th 1961.

The dated records have been in June (8), July (11), August (6), September (4), November (2). On three occasions two birds were together. Counties represented in the records are Cork (1), Kerry (4), Clare (3), Tipperary (2), Wexford (4), Dublin (6), Meath (1), Galway (2), Mayo (4), Monaghan (1), Down (3), Antrim (1), Derry (2), Donegal (6).

Red-eyed Vireo: *Vireo olivaceus*

One record.

One was picked up dead on October 4th 1951 at Tuskar Rock,

Co. Wexford, where it had evidently been killed as a result of striking the lighthouse. The specimen is in the National Museum.

Scarlet Tanager: *Piranga olivacea*

One record.

A female was trapped at Copeland Bird Observatory, Co. Down, on October 12th 1963.

The bill measurements of the bird appear to exceed the normal range of the species. While all other characters fit this tanager, the record is still *sub judice*, with the remote possibility that the bird was a Summer Tanager, *P. rubra*.

Hawfinch: *Coccothraustes coccothraustes*

Formerly regular winter visitor, now a vagrant.

About 1900 the Hawfinch became rare as a winter visitor and since 1911 there have been only about eleven records from such widely separated counties as Dublin, Cork, Kerry, Antrim, Mayo and Galway. One in Leix in April 1934 was joined by a second in May, but no evidence of breeding was found.

At Straffan, Co. Kildare, Hawfinches were present throughout the breeding seasons of 1896 to 1902 and in 1902 an adult was seen feeding young.

Since 1911 the months of occurrence have been October (3), November (3), February (2), April, May and June (one each).

The most recent record is of a female on Inishbofin, Co. Galway, on October 10th 1957.

Greenfinch: *Chloris chloris*

Resident. Passage migrant. Possibly winter visitor.

This is a very common resident species, breeding in all counties and on some marine islands, though not on those off the Connacht coast, except Achill. It has recently become established as a breeding bird on the Mullet and in western Donegal. The Dingle Peninsula in Kerry is well populated.

The size of autumn and winter flocks seen in western counties is not comparable with those in eastern counties. From light-stations and observatories comes evidence of passage migration in September and October and on a smaller scale from March to May.

It is possible that the rather larger numbers seen on the east coast in November may include winter visitors, but there is little indication of general increase in winter.

In the past few years there is some evidence that numbers have diminished.

Goldfinch: *Carduelis carduelis*

Resident. Winter visitor.

The Goldfinch breeds in every county. During the past thirty years it has increased in some localities and has extended its range. It now breeds on Achill Island and the Aran Islands. In Co. Kerry the numbers breeding have increased. On the other hand, in some counties, particularly those in the east, it has decreased and is nowadays sparsely distributed.

Immigration, commencing in late September, is well marked in October, more so in November when fifty in a day have been recorded at Great Saltee, Co. Wexford. On September 28th 1959 a flock of about 300 was seen on the Wexford coast.

Birds seen at isolated stations in March, April and May are presumably emigrants.

So far there is no evidence that Ireland receives any immigrants from the Continent.

Considerable flocks sometimes containing up to 200 birds occur in winter.

Siskin: *Carduelis spinus*

Resident. Probable winter visitor.

Siskins breed in all the provinces but their distribution is extremely local and the numbers doing so fluctuate.

The breeding range has expanded within the past fifty years; it now embraces Connemara. In Co. Mayo the spread has been remarkable and similarly in parts of Co. Kerry. In Donegal the breeding range has expanded, but in this county and in several others a serious decline in numbers has been noticed in recent years.

After the breeding season and during winter, flocks containing twenty or more birds are locally common.

Records of migrants are somewhat irregular and the numbers fluctuate greatly. For instance there was heavy migration at Cape Clear and Great Saltee in October and November 1959. It seems possible that this irruptive form of migration, noticed in several years at coastal stations, may have some bearing on the fluctuations in strength of the breeding population.

Linnet: *Carduelis cannabina*

Resident. Passage migrant.

Linnets are very common and to be seen almost anywhere. They breed in every county and on all suitable marine islands.

Their passage migration in autumn is very heavy. It may start at the end of August, the volume increases in September and its peak is reached at the end of that month and early in October. The maximum number noted at Great Saltee in a day has been five hundred, but often two or three hundred have been recorded. These, like the great numbers that build up at Carnsore Point a little farther north on the Wexford coast, are seen to depart southward over the sea. Concurrently passage has been noticed at the Copeland Islands off Co. Down and on the Co. Dublin coast.

Linnets, sometimes in numbers reaching six hundred have been seen in October when they arrive at Malin Head, Co. Donegal from over the sea and continue their flight southward.

Movement on the Wexford coast in April and May is on a much smaller scale, but at Cape Clear, Co. Cork numbers up to one hundred and forty have been recorded; some coming from over the sea have been noted, the birds continuing on a northward course.

Perhaps some immigrants arrive in autumn and winter, but so far proof is lacking and the large scale movements are undoubtedly of passage birds.

Twite: *Carduelis flavirostris*

Resident. Possibly a winter visitor and/or passage migrant.

The Twite inhabits the wild and exposed parts of Ireland, especially the cliffs of the western coasts and marine islands. Some inhabit inland mountainous districts.

Flocks form after the breeding season and in autumn and winter are found not infrequently in lowland areas and often at the shores of tidal bays and estuaries, even on the east coast.

Specimens have been obtained in autumn and winter from light-stations off Cos. Donegal and Kerry and once off Co. Wexford. More significant is the evidence of migration in April, May, September and October at Tory Island where numbers up to a hundred have been seen in autumn. At Malin Head, also in Co. Donegal, Twites have been seen arriving over the sea from the north-east in September and October.

On one occasion at Cape Clear, Co. Cork, a flock of fourteen flew out over the sea to the south-west on October 30th.

Much remains to be learned about the migrations of this species.

Redpoll: *Carduelis flammea*

Lesser Redpoll: *Carduelis flammea cabaret*

Resident.

The Lesser Redpoll is a widely distributed species breeding, though somewhat locally, in every county.

Flocks occur in autumn and winter and it is often mid-May before these break up. The winter flocks wander locally.

Migrations are perplexing and no definite pattern emerges. Birds of this race have occurred, usually singly, at Great Saltee in April, May and November; at Tory Island in May; at Copeland in March and September.

In addition, Redpolls which could not definitely be assigned to this race have visited all the above stations, and also Inishtrahull and Cape Clear, in spring and autumn.

On October 7th 1960 over twenty-five were at Copeland, over fifteen on October 29th 1961.

Mealy Redpoll: *Carduelis flammea flammea*

Vagrant. Possibly an irregular passage migrant.

This form has been identified with certainty about eleven times in autumn and winter.

On Achill Island a flock of about eight appeared in the winter 1892–93 and for a week in mid-October 1898 small parties were present.

Other reports have been of birds obtained in widely separated localities.

Some, if not all of a flock of fifteen Redpolls seen in Co. Armagh in January 1957 were of this form.

It is not known in how many cases the records of migrants seen at isolated stations mentioned under *C. f. cabaret* might have been of this form.

Redpolls having the characters of one of the 'northern' forms, probably *C. hornemanni*, were reported as follows: five in Co. Armagh, December 24th 1958; two, Duncrue Street marsh, Belfast, Co. Antrim, January 11th 1958. One at Malin Head, Co. Donegal, on October 21st 1961, in company of Lesser Redpolls, was on size believed to be of the race *Carduelis hornemanni exilipes*.

Greenland Redpoll: *Carduelis flammea rostrata*
Vagrant.

There are at least eleven records of this race, reported most often on the coasts of Donegal, Mayo and Kerry and in the months September (at least 8), October (1), November (1). On May 20th 1942 a male was found dead at Eagle Island lighthouse, Co. Mayo.

Occurrences have been of single birds or two together, but on September 12th and 13th 1955 at least ten having the characteristics of this race were on Tory Island and five on September 11th 1960.

Birds undoubtedly of this race were seen in September 1954 on Tory Island, but no details of numbers are available.

Serin: *Serinus canarius*
Four records.

One was captured by bird catchers in Co. Dublin in January 1893, another, a male, on February 1st 1907. One was seen and heard singing at Fermoy, Co. Cork, in May 1947. One was seen at Cape Clear, Co. Cork, on October 4th 1959.

Bullfinch: *Pyrrhula pyrrhula*
Resident.

This species has gradually been extending its range westward and has during the past three years shown a tremendous increase, not only in the breeding population, but in the numbers seen in winter.

The increase has been reported chiefly from the southern half of Ireland. In Co. Wexford it has been very noticeable; on November 8th 1964 a single flock contained twenty-two birds.

There is no satisfactory evidence of migration, yet numbers up to four have been seen at isolated stations off the north-east, south-east and south-west coasts in April and October.

At Copeland off Co. Down there were two on June 9th and another on 16th. Individuals trapped at Cape Clear in October and at Great Saltee in April were referable to the race *Pyrrhula p. nesa.*

In Connacht a perplexing movement has been noticed on dates between October 18th and November 6th in several years. Birds are seen flying very high, direction is sometimes indefinite, but often they arrive from the north or north-west. Very small numbers are involved, but on October 29th 1964 a flock of twenty arrived at Black Head, Co. Clare, coming in fairly high over the sea and from the north-west. They landed, joining others already scattered in the area. After a short while all flew away southward.

Scarlet Grosbeak: *Carpodacus erythrinus*
Two records.

A female or immature bird was seen on September 8th 1954 on Tory Island, Co. Donegal, another on Great Saltee, Co. Wexford, on August 31st 1958. The latter was trapped; it remained on the island until September 4th.

Rose-breasted Grosbeak: *Pheucticus ludovicianus*
Two records.

An adult male was seen at Shane's Castle, Co. Antrim, on November 24th 1957. A first-winter male was seen at Cape Clear, Co. Cork, on October 7th and 8th 1962.

Crossbill: *Loxia curvirostra*

Possibly resident. Irruptions occur periodically. Small numbers probably visit Ireland annually.

It will be seen from the above how much still remains to be learnt about our Crossbills.

Following irruptions in the past, Crossbills became locally resident. The status has been unstable, for the breeding population following an irruption has invariably decreased until augmented by a subsequent irruption.

That of 1888 resulted in a considerable increase in breeding birds and a few years later Crossbills were breeding in eighteen counties.

From 1937 there followed a decline in breeding birds which the irruptions of 1953, 1958 and 1962 did little or nothing to restore.

In 1962 the invasion was on a notable scale, being very widespread from the end of June onwards. Flocks were the largest ever recorded in Ireland, some being of over 100 birds; in one wood in Co. Wicklow at least 250 were present. Some were seen as late as November and in May and June 1963 but there was no absolute proof of breeding.

In 1957 at least one pair bred at Parkanaur, Co. Tyrone. Breeding, falling just short of proof, has been suspected in recent years in Co. Wicklow and almost certainly occurred in Co. Down in 1964.

Small numbers are seen irregularly in summer.

Parrot Crossbill: *Loxia pytyopsittacus*

Two possible records.

Five crossbills at Tory Island, Co. Donegal, on October 15th 1962 were believed to be of this species, as were about twenty crossbills seen at Cushendall, Co. Antrim, on April 11th 1963.

In both instances the bills showed the heaviness characteristic of the species. It should be borne in mind that in the autumn of 1962 many Parrot Crossbills visited northern Britain. At the same time the variation in bill-depth in crossbills indicates the possibility of an overlap.

Two-barred Crossbill: *Loxia leucoptera*
Four records.

A female was shot at Grenville near Belfast on January 11th 1802. A female was killed in Co. Antrim about 1867. An adult male was shot at Tempo Manor, Co. Fermanagh, on February 17th 1895. An adult male was shot near Crumlin, Co. Antrim, on August 2nd 1927.

Chaffinch: *Fringilla coelebs*

Chaffinch: *Fringilla coelebs gengleri*
Resident. Winter visitor.

This is the race of Chaffinch which breeds in every county and wherever there are trees or bushes.

Flocks form in autumn and move about the country haunting for the most part farmyards and their vicinity. There is no evidence that our breeding stock emigrates. The few seen at Great Saltee, Co. Wexford, in October and November are perhaps immigrants.

Chaffinch: *Fringilla coelebs coelebs*
Autumn passage migrant. Winter visitor.

There is passage in autumn of this form chiefly on the east coast and on the coast of Co. Wexford. The numbers that are seen vary considerably from year to year. A small number, but again varying annually, winters in Ireland, even as far west as Co. Mayo.

One ringed in Co. Dublin in February was recovered in Sweden within the breeding range of this form.

Continental Chaffinch: *Fringilla coelebs hortensis*
Winter visitor.

This race pours into Ireland and in winter is found throughout the country in flocks that sometimes contain several hundred birds.

It haunts woods, stubbles, rough neglected fields and root crops.

Immigration commences about mid-October. It is at its height in early November when up to a thousand in a day have been recorded at Great Saltee, Co. Wexford.

The race has been identified at Copeland Bird Observatory, Co. Down, and has been seen arriving over the sea in small numbers at Malin Head, Co. Donegal.

In some years a remarkable migration is observed on a very narrow front stretching south-eastwards across Co. Mayo from Erris Head where, on occasion, hundreds have been watched arriving over the sea.

This movement is seen on a large scale only in periods of strong south-east winds and only if they occur during the last ten days of October. The birds have been definitely identified as of this race.

The winter visitors depart in mid-March.

Birds ringed in Ireland in winter as belonging to this race have been recovered in its breeding range and vice versa.

Brambling: *Fringilla montifringilla*

Winter visitor.

The Brambling comes in varying numbers to all the provinces, but least to Connacht where it is scarce.

The species is present from October to March, but sometimes it is seen in September and in April. November is the chief month of immigration.

Numbers fluctuate. Recently the winters of 1949–50 and 1952–53 had unusually large numbers. In the latter winter flocks of 100 and 300 were counted in Cos. Down and Wicklow respectively.

Single birds have been seen in Co. Down on June 13th and on Great Skellig, Co. Kerry, from July 8th to 15th.

Fox Sparrow: *Passerella iliaca*

One record.

One having affinity to the Eastern Fox Sparrow (*P. i. iliaca*) was trapped at Copeland Bird Observatory, Co. Down, on June 3rd 1961.

Corn Bunting: *Emberiza calandra*

Resident.

About 1900 the Corn Bunting was breeding in every county except Leitrim.

It has rapidly decreased and is no longer found, except as a non-breeding stray, in any inland haunt. Even on the coasts it has become a scarce and extremely local breeding bird. It is perhaps more plentiful in western Kerry than elsewhere. It has diminished to negligible numbers on Achill and the Mullet, Co. Mayo, and Inishbofin, where in 1945 it still flourished.

Individuals have been observed at isolated coastal stations in March, April, May and September in recent years and outside the breeding season flocks of up to fifteen birds are sometimes seen on headlands.

Yellowhammer: *Emberiza citrinella*
Resident.

Yellowhammers are widely distributed in every county. In some localities the numbers have decreased and the bird has withdrawn from some islands off the west coast and from Rathlin Island.

Flocks form after the breeding season. In autumn large numbers suddenly appear locally. Over 90 and over 500 have been seen on two days in separate years in a restricted area at Malin Head, Co. Donegal, in September and October, their activities suggesting movements of an irruptive nature. No actual arrival was witnessed.

Yellowhammers have visited, singly or in twos and threes, Great Saltee, Co. Wexford, and Copeland, Co. Down, in March, April and May and Tory Island, Co. Donegal, in April and May.

There is some evidence of movement on the east coast in autumn. It is difficult to interpret any of the foregoing movements.

Black-headed Bunting: *Emberiza melanocephala*
Two records.

A male was seen at Great Saltee, Co. Wexford, on May 31st 1950. One was seen at Ballymore, Co. Wexford, on November 28th 1958.

Red-headed Bunting: *Emberiza bruniceps*
Seven records.

Single birds have been seen at Great Saltee, Co. Wexford, on

September 22nd and 23rd 1951; Tory Island, Co. Donegal, April 26th 1953; near Belmullet, Co. Mayo, June 8th 1953; on Inishtrahull, Co. Donegal, September 10th 1953; at Great Saltee on May 5th 1962; at Cape Clear, Co. Cork, July 26th 1962, and another there on September 14th 1964. All were males.

Occurrences of this species are always suspect of being 'escapes' and without doubt some were such. One or two were thought to be genuine migrants.

Yellow-breasted Bunting: *Emberiza aureola*

Two records.

One was seen on Tory Island, Co. Donegal, on September 18th 1959. A male was seen at Cape Clear, Co. Cork, on October 11th 1961.

Cirl Bunting: *Emberiza cirlus*

One record.

One was closely watched and its note clearly heard, near Dunfanaghy, Co. Donegal, on August 2nd 1902.

Ortolan Bunting: *Emberiza hortulana*

Passage migrant.

Since 1951 this bunting has been reported almost annually. Occurrences have been in April (1), May (2), August (4), September (14), October (7).

Most often one to four are recorded in a year, but in 1960 there were ten reports and in 1961 six. The majority of occurrences have been of single birds.

Except for two seen on the Co. Wicklow coast, one beside Belfast Lough, one at Erris Head, Co. Mayo, one at Tory Island and one at Inishtrahull, Co. Donegal, all reports have come from Cape Clear Island and Great Saltee.

Rustic Bunting: *Emberiza rustica*
One record.

A male was seen on Cape Clear Island, Co. Cork, on October 9th 1959.

Little Bunting: *Emberiza pusilla*
Ten records.

A female was killed against Rockabill lighthouse, Co. Dublin, on October 2nd 1908. One was seen at Rineanna on the Co. Clare coast on September 26th 1949. One was seen at Malahide, Co. Dublin, on December 5th 1949. One entered a house on Tory Island, Co. Donegal, in the first week of November 1952; on examination it was considered to be a first-winter male. One was seen at Great Saltee, Co. Wexford, on September 17th 1953; one was trapped there on April 16th 1957. One was seen beside Rogerstown estuary, Co. Dublin, on October 24th 1954. One was seen on the north shore of Belfast Lough, Co. Antrim, on September 25th 1955. One was seen at Baldoyle, Co. Dublin, on February 20th 1957. A first-winter bird was trapped at Tory Island on October 6th 1961.

Thus the occurrences have been in February (1), April (1), September (3), October (3), November (1), December (1).

Reed Bunting: *Emberiza schoeniclus*
Resident.

Reed Buntings breed commonly in every county wherever there is suitable habitat. They also breed on marine islands.

In winter flocks haunt roadside hedges and are sometimes found on high moors.

There is no clear picture of migration. Specimens have been obtained at light-stations in spring and autumn and individuals or parties of up to four birds have been seen at Great Saltee, Co. Wexford, in April, May, October and November, most often in the two last named months. At Cape Clear, Co. Cork, there is but meagre evidence of movement in March, September and October, also at

Copeland, Co. Down, in April and October and at Tory Island, Co. Donegal, in April.

In addition, the same irruptive form of behaviour as in the case of the Yellowhammer has been noticed at Malin Head, Co. Donegal, where on September 28th 1963 over 350 were seen moving about in the area.

Lapland Bunting: *Calcarius lapponicus*

Passage migrant. Occasional in winter.

The Lapland Bunting is an annual passage migrant in fluctuating numbers. In 1953 the exceptional total of about 300 was recorded in early September in a restricted area in northern Donegal.

This species arrives on the north and more particularly on the north-west coast chiefly in September and October. It has once been recorded as early as August 27th when, in 1959, about twenty arrived on that date.

In several autumns when observers were at Erris Head, Co. Mayo, a maximum of over twenty-five were seen once on September 11th. A few have been noted on Inishbofin, Co. Galway, in September.

At Cape Clear, Co. Cork, and at Great Saltee, Co. Wexford, the species is irregularly recorded and in single numbers only. There is a record for Co. Down and two of migrants on the Dublin coast.

After being so noticeable at their arrival points in Co. Donegal, it is strange that so few are seen during their passage. All records have been for coastal areas.

At Tory Island, Co. Donegal, the daily maximum over a number of years has varied between ten and seventy birds; over twenty in a day are quite frequent.

Winter records are few. One was caught at Kilbarrack, Co. Dublin, in January 1906, another in December 1907 and one at Killough, Co. Down, in January 1916.

Five were present beside Wexford Harbour in January and February 1962, quite possibly for a longer period.

Spring records are very scarce and have been at Tory Island in April and May and at Cape Clear once, in April.

Snow Bunting: *Plectrophenax nivalis*
Winter visitor. Recorded in every month.

As a winter visitor the Snow Bunting occurs in fluctuating numbers. The north and west coasts receive the majority, but the bird is found in all maritime counties.

It is frequent on mountains near the coast and has occasionally been seen in other inland places.

In winters when they are particularly numerous, flocks of between 150 and 200 birds are seen. It is more usual to find flocks containing about twenty birds.

Due to the fact that Snow Buntings can be met with in every month the citing of actual dates of arrival and departure is impossible. The majority, however, arrive towards the end of September and numbers continue to build up into November.

Departure takes place from mid-March to mid-April. In the north-west the bird is often still quite plentiful in May.

Slate-coloured Junco: *Junco hyemalis*
One record.

One shot on May 30th 1905 at Loop Head, Co. Clare, is in the National Museum.

There is no reason for supposing that it was not a genuine vagrant.

House Sparrow: *Passer domesticus*
Resident.

Although breeding in every county the House Sparrow is of very local distribution in some localities and absent from areas where it might be expected.

It inhabits some of the most exposed inhabited marine islands, yet is scarce in most of the coastal districts of Cos. Clare, Galway and Mayo.

A decrease which set in before 1950, especially in the far west, has continued recently. It is thought that this decrease, in part at least, has arisen from the replacement of thatched roofs by slate ones.

Local movements take place after the breeding season. Individuals and even flocks have been seen at light-stations off every coast and an individual once in April at Great Saltee, Co. Wexford.

Tree Sparrow: *Passer montanus*
Resident.

Always formerly a very local resident, the Tree Sparrow had colonies on the Co. Dublin coast and in about five places on the western seaboard. By 1950 most of these had disappeared.

By 1956 the one remaining Co. Donegal colony no longer existed. In 1955 a few pairs bred in Co. Derry and off the coast of Co. Down in 1956. In 1957 and 1958 a few bred at the Gobbins, Co. Antrim.

From then until 1961 there were occasional scattered records but no proof of breeding.

Then in 1961 came reports of breeding in Cos. Mayo, Derry and on Tory Island, Co. Donegal. In that year too there were several migration records from Copeland, Tory Island and St. John's Point, Co. Down. In a restricted area at Malin Head, Co. Donegal, about fifty were seen in October.

In 1962 repopulation on a widespread scale was noticed. Breeding was proved in Co. Dublin near where up to forty birds had wintered; in Co. Down at St. John's Point where fifty-five had been seen in March.

This remarkable resurgence has continued.

In 1964 breeding was known in thirteen counties:—Antrim: Portrush, the Gobbins and Shane's Castle (circumstantial evidence). Armagh: near Lough Neagh, in willow trees. Down: St. John's Point, some nests being in trees. Louth: Carlingford Abbey, near Greenore, Ballug Castle. Dublin: Lowther Lodge, Balbriggan, Skerries, Baldongan Castle, Feltrim. Wicklow: Grey Fort and willow trees near Kilcoole. Wexford: Castletown, Clougheast Castle, Ballytrent. Waterford: near Brownstown Head. Galway: Bunowen Castle, Bunowen Harbour, Ardfry (in trees). Mayo: Inishkea, Surgeview near Blacksod, Castle Lacken. Sligo: ruins at Raghly. Donegal: Tory Island, near Newtown Cunningham.

Derry: in trees near Lough Beg. Breeding suspected on the coast of this county.

In 1965 the whole Lough Neagh basin had been thinly populated. In the same year breeding was established in Co. Cork at Roche's Point and at a headland east of Trabolgan House.

Additional breeding stations were found in Co. Mayo at and near Annagh Head on the Mullet and breeding at Rosserk Abbey was probable: Wexford: Begerin farm on the North Slob, probably since 1964. Donegal: Malin Head. Antrim: near Glenavy.

There may be further stations for Tree Sparrows have been seen in the breeding season in several places far removed from known nesting sites.

Our Tree Sparrows show a marked preference for ruined buildings such as old castles, coastguard stations, mansions and even ruined cottages in which to breed. Only in very recent years have they been using willow trees or dead trees.

It is very noticeable that, without exception, nesting sites are always chosen having within sight a measurable expanse of water; except the few inland sites (also near water) all other colonies are on the sea coastal fringe. In some cases cliffs are used.

Colonies are all small, usually consisting of less than six pairs, often only one pair is found. The St. John's Point colony of about twelve pairs is probably the largest.

Very intensive search of the many promising sites in Cos. Clare, Limerick, Kerry and Cork has yielded only negative results, though in Cork and Kerry there have been records of individuals.

ADDENDA

Sea-bird migration, p. 27—The following are results obtained from an analysis based on variable monthly amounts of sea-watching at Cape Clear, Co. Cork, during the seven years 1959 to 1965. They probably give a strong indication of the normal picture of peak periods of passage of the following species.

Balearic Shearwater, p. 37—Beginning of April. Less marked at the beginning of October.
Sooty Shearwater, p. 39—Beginning of September. (A few only are recorded in spring.)
Common Scoter, p. 57—End of February; maximum peak at the end of June: end of November.
Great Skua, p. 110—Beginning of April. Beginning of September.
Arctic Skua, p. 111—End of May. A very small peak at the end of September.
Pomarine Skua, p. 111—Beginning of May. Less marked peak at the beginning of October.

The Committee of Cape Clear Bird Observatory has kindly permitted the use of the above information.

Wilson's Petrel, p. 34—The birds were obtained at the time of an exceptionally large scale 'wreck' of Leach's Petrels.
Glossy Ibis, p. 45—One shot in Co. Galway on December 5th 1965 is the first record since 1959 and forms the second December occurrence.
Velvet Scoter, p. 56—September records now number nine: three females were seen in flight off Old Head, Kinsale, Co. Cork in September 1965.
Common Scoter, p. 57—The number now wintering in Killala Bay does not appear to exceed 100.

In the north-east corner of Donegal Bay over 500 are found in winter.

Red-necked Phalarope, p. 108—In 1965 three were seen on autumn passage in October.
Waxwing, p. 178—On page 179 the mention of 300 birds on the shores of Lough Erne it now transpires was of a flock seen in Enniskillen, Co. Fermanagh and estimated at 300.
Bullfinch, p. 187—A male of the nominate race, *Pyrrhula p. pyrrhula* was trapped at Ballinasloe, Co. Galway on February 14th 1965. *Pyrrhula p. nesa* is the form to which our breeding stock belongs.
Scarlet Grosbeak, p. 187—A female or immature bird was seen at Inishtrahull, Co. Donegal on September 25th 1965.

INDEX TO SYSTEMATIC LIST OF BIRDS